t R

REE

A "Getting to Know You" Guide

CW00557129

Great Barrier Reef
Ningaloo Reef
Indonesia Archipelago
Malaysia
Papua New Guinea,
Fiji & South Pacific Islands
Maldives
Micronesia
Thailand
Phillippines

OceanNEnvironment
Proceeds from this book
contribute to Save Our Seas Fund

With Tips on Underwater Photography

Michael Aw

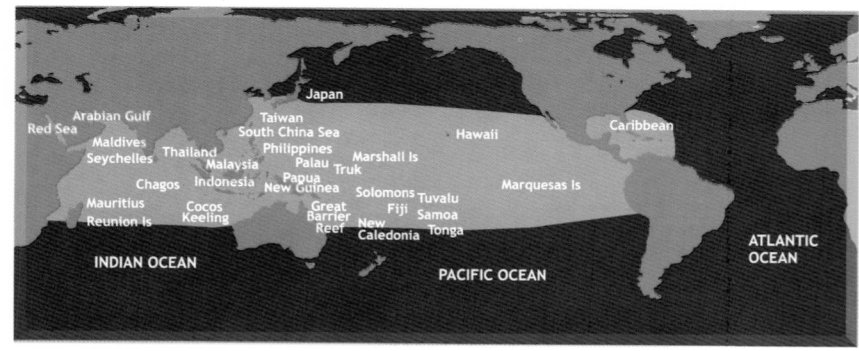

Nature's Richest Realm

The moment I put my head beneath the surface of a tropical reef, I slip into a different world; habitats within habitats where the abundance of it's inhabitants envelops me in totality. I am engulfed immediately in a rich liquid field of energy, an invisible web connecting all life both in the sea and on the land. This is the window to the pulse of this planet. I see beings of our ancestry, very closely related to those which thrived nearly half a billion years ago. Tropical coral reefs are the oldest natural communities still living on earth. Some reef animals known today are almost unchanged from those found in fossils dating from the age of the dinosaurs, some 100 million years ago. The tropical reef contains our planet's most spectacular forests, a surrealistic landscape of blue surrounded by life. Life in a hundred thousand forms; lush gardens of the sea supporting astounding numbers in a densely packed, thriving marine metropolis. Coral reefs have the largest abundance and greatest diversity of life living together compared to any place on Earth, including the tropical rain forest. Every phylum from the tiniest bacteria, sponges, coral to fish, reptiles, birds and mammals are all inhabitants of the coral reef.

Coral reefs are the Piccadilly Circus, Manhattans or King Crosses of the ocean; they are an oasis in the blue desert, a place which gives shelter and food in an ocean where the essential necessities of life are scarce. The reef itself is a living, growing organism comprised of animals all working together to create the largest biological structure on earth- so enormous that it is nature's only monument visible from space. This is the most complex realm known to mankind, a food web sustained by the network of life in the tropical reef. In fact, the entire tropical ocean ecosystem relies on the reefs for sustenance and likewise, all life on land is dependent on the ocean for its survival. Frequent upwellings from the deep brings rich nutrients for phytoplankton (plants) to grow which in turn provides sustenance for zooplankton comprising of tiny offspring from the animal, pelagic and coral reef realms. The mangrove forests around coastal islands are nursery for both reef fishes and invertebrates.

A coral reef is basically a consolidated lump of limestone laid down by the skeletons of corals and cementing plants, the coralline algae, over hundreds or thousands of years. A veneer of living corals and other reef organisms indicates that this process is ongoing. Hidden within this apparently dead structure are animals and plants which burrow and dig: worms, sponges, mussels, bacteria and algae, all of which play a part in restructuring and cementing the limestone. Life on a coral reef consists of a myriad of networks sustaining communities of organisms with complex interrelationships. Reef animals and plants demonstrate an incredible form of adaptive behavior in varied habitats, abilities to cope with a variety of predators, a broad range of food sources and amazing mechanisms in form and function.

The key to survival of species revolves around the dynamics of commensalism, symbiotic relationships and the efficiencies of recycling. Every part of the reef is serviced by a variety of organisms, every second, every minute, every day, every season. If one fails, another takes over; it may not be who should do the job but the job gets done. Reef communities of plants and animals are generally divided into the reef builders and the reef dwellers. The reef builders are those organisms responsible for the development of the reef such as hard coral and calcareous algae. Their limestone skeletons form the superstructure or framework of a coral reef. Plants and animals form a symbiotic relationship by utilizing the waste of other animals and photosynthesis provides the coral with nutrition to grow. Reef dwellers do not contribute to the building of the framework but they do play a vital role in the transfer of energy through the community's food web. In exchange, the superstructure of the reef provides them with the protection of a shelter. The bodies of sea urchins and sea shells consist of limestone components and they are contributors to reef building when deceased.

Corals, sponges, sea anemones, tubeworms and feather stars are plankton feeders, filtering nutrients brought in by an endless stream of intertidal currents. These animals contribute to reef building and some of them are preyed upon by reef fishes. Swarms of fishes shower their faeces across the reef which are then quickly devoured by other fishes or when settled are also devoured by bottom corals supplying their zooxanthellae with nitrates and phosphates, the necessary nutrition for growth. Organic matter and sediment produced by fishes settles to the bottom and becomes a food source for the millions of inhabitants on the bottom of the ocean. Sea cucumbers, shrimp, crabs, bottom dwelling fishes and sea shells are some of the prominent ones which scavenge through layers and layers of sand. All resources are recycled, nothing is wasted. Marine invertebrates and fishes release their eggs and sperm which float to the surface of the ocean before settling down to live on the reef. The top layer of the sea is a 'seafood soup' created by the many mothers of the reef. This soup is the staple diet of many marine mammals, pelagic fishes including invertebrates and fishes of the reef. Life cycles of the coral reef epitomize nature's commitment to the concept of Recycling. It is sad that we exist in what we call civilized societies, yet know so little and care so little about our connections to the sea. There are many field reference books which describe and help identification - this one takes you beyond. With our pictures and research texts, we hope to introduce you to their lifestyles, the way they live and how they live.

There are three basic types of coral reefs; **fringing reefs**, **barrier reefs** and **atolls**. Fringing reefs are found below the rocky or sandy shores of land and occur around islands and coasts. Barrier reefs occur well offshore and are largely independent of land, growing from the seafloor. They are the result of thousands or even millions of years of reef building by corals and coralline algae. Barrier reefs can sometimes contain small islands, known as coral cays, which are formed from deposits of reef material. The third basic type of reef, the atoll, is found in the deep open ocean and is the result of a coral reef growing on top of a volcanic sea mountain which has since subsided. Within a reef, there are usually a number of habitats or zones that have quite different water and light conditions and therefore quite different types of coral species.

The shallowest part of the reef is usually the Reef Flat and this zone often dries at low tide. As the name suggests it is a flat, featureless area and it is usually inhabited by coral species which can tolerate strong light and some drying. Across the outer margin of the reef flat is the Reef Edge, an area which usually bears the brunt of the wave action and is inhabited by robust corals. Moving deeper off the reef edge leads to the Reef Slope, where the depth increases rapidly and the wave action drops off. This area is often cut by channels and ridges and the light and water conditions can be quite variable. This variability is mirrored in the range of coral species which occur here, with some species adapted to strong currents and light while others thrive in deeper, more protected waters. The Reef Wall is an extreme version of the Reef Slope dropping straight off into deep water as a sheer face. Finally, the Submerged Reef is a separate reef which occurs in deeper waters, usually out from the Reef Slope and is simply a coral ridge growing from the sea floor.

Reef slope

Channel, soft coral growth in o

Reef Zones

"Fringing Reef"

Reef Edge

Lagoon

Reef Wall

Reef edge - fringing reef

nang

Reef slope - barrier reef

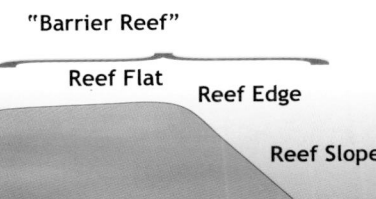

"Barrier Reef"

Reef Flat

Reef Edge

Reef Slope

Submerged Reef

Author & Photographer:
Michael Aw
Executive Editor:
Alison Redhead

Scientific Advisors:
Dr. Carden Wallace
Jacki Wolstenholme
Shane Ah'yong
Dr. Penny Berrent
Consulting Editor:
Jodie Lee

Colour Production:
NamMei Loh

Art Direction & Picture Editor:
Michael Aw

Published for
OceanNEnvironment Ltd
P.O.Box 2138, Carlingford Court Post Office
Carlingford, NSW 2118, Australia
Email: oneocean@OceanNEnvironment.com.au
www.OceanNEnvironment.com.au
Produced by Ocean Geographic
All photographs & Text are Copyright Michael AW ©
www.MichawlAW.com

First published 10/1997
Second Edition: 10/2001
<u>**National Library of Australia Cataloguing-in Publication Entry**</u>
<u>**Michael AW**</u>
<u>**Tropical Reef Life** - a marine awareness guide</u>
<u>ISBN 0 646 310 143</u>

We human beings, sitting on the top of the food chain, hold absolute power to save a species or drive it into extinction - something we have accomplished and excelled in on far too many occasions. With a brief survey of the Red List published by the World Conservation Monitoring Centre, our records are impressive; nearly all species of sea turtles are critically endangered, slaughtered to satisfy the insatiable hunger of many, from the royal and wealthy to the paupers of, so they say, indigenous people. Then there are the Sumatran and Siberian tigers, hunted to enhance the libido of the pea-minded - it is predicted that by the year 2000, all tigers will be extinct from the wild. Turtles, dolphins, pandas and orang utans are all alike, though not necessarily for most superficial reasons, they are pet projects for wildlife savers. When dolphins were shown on national television drowning in tuna nets, the public rallied, Save and Adopt the Dolphins campaigns mushroomed all over the world. But what about the tuna? We have missed the boat completely. Fisherman and their children in the Philippines and Indonesia are enticed to decimate the Napoleon wrasse population with cyanide just to supply the lucrative live fish trade in Hong Kong and Asian capitals. The traders prosper, the wealthy feast, the reef dies, there are no Save the Napoleon Wrasse Campaigns - like the tunas, they are just another fish. It seems in this world, you have to beautiful, cute or big and bad to earn the right to recognition and salvation.

Recently I met a couple of staff from a popular dive operation wearing the shop's T-shirt with the words "Save the Reef" printed boldly on the back. When I asked them why, their replies were; "My boss says so" and " it attracts the guests to buy one!". How can we demand of people as well as our children to save the environment which they know so little about or have so little association with. In an analogy, we unconditionally protect our kin and old pooch because we have learnt to appreciate and love them, likewise people can only protect and preserve the reef if they have an affinity with the animals of the marine environment. In this book, you will discover about the more prominent members of the coral reef societies; their choice of homes, their habits, their social hierarchy within the intricacies of everyday life on the reef. Some of them are capable of striking faster than a bullet, some have super-visionary power while some species are like our legends and heroes; undertaking ultimate sacrifices so that their next generation may live. Some practise parental care while some adopt a bohemic lifestyle like a sailor with wife at every port. A Marine Awareness Guide to Tropical Reef Life is only a brief insight into their world, but like Tropical Reef Fishes, we hope that this book will enhance your awareness and develop your love affair with the sea. Michael AW

Understanding, Appreciation and Love
Begets Preservation and Protection

OceanNEnvironment

Simple Phylogenetic Classification of Reef Animals

Phylum Protozoa - single celled animals

Phylum Porifera   Sponges

Phylum Cnidarian - corals, soft corals, black corals

Hydroids, sea jellies, gorgonians,

Anemones, sea whips, sea pens

Hard Coral

Soft Coral, zoanthids

Phylum Platyhelminthes & Annelida (Flat & segmented worms)

Phylum Mollusca, sea snails, chitons,

Nudibranchs, bivalves

Cephlapods -Cuttlefish, Squid, Octopus

Phylum Bryozoa (Moss animals)

Phylum Arthropoda - insects, crustaceans,

Sea spiders

Phylum Echinodermata

Feather stars

Brittle stars

Sea Urchins

Sea Cucumbers

Subphylum Cephalochordata - sea squirts or Ascidians

Subphylum vertebrata - sharks, rays and bony fishes *

See Tropical Reef Fishes - A Marine Awareness Guide
published 1994, Ocean Geographic

What is in a Name:

Scientists use a unique system, devised by Carl Linnaeus in the 18th century, to give names to orga
which language a book is written in the species remains the same name and therefore can be reco
the system is referred to as "binominal nomenclature". In the context of this book, we use the w
kingdom. The species name of an animal is the name for members of the unique group of interbr
of separate species with many similar external and internal features. The family is then compose
common line of ancestry. The scientific names in this are book italicized. The first part is the g
species or specific name, all in lower case. An easy example is: Family name: Acroporidae - all rel
gemmifera - the unique species *Acropora gemmifera*

CONTENTS

in Latin throughout the entire world. Thus, it does not matter
d by all countries. Each name comprises two Latin words and
hylum which refers to the roots of the organism in the animal
g animals to which it belongs. A genus is composed of a group
all genera that have overall similar characteristics and share a
name commencing with a capital letter and the second is the
staghorn corals. Genus: Acropora - staghorn coral. Species:

Staghorn coral , *Acropora gemmifera*
60mm / f5.6, 1/ 60   Togian, Nth Sulawesi

One evening eight years ago, as I was about to slip away to shoot another roll at a shoot-out competition in Flores, Indonesia, Gerard Soury, a French judge came up to me to offer encouragement; "I wish you make some nice pictures". It might be in the French vocabulary to best describe 'taking photographs' as 'making pictures', but since that day, I have adopted the 'making pictures' attitude in my approach to photography.

Underwater photography is truly an art form, a craft resulting from the union of art and science. However, if you compare a painting to an underwater picture, the latter is far more difficult to accomplish. On top of creative acumen, it is a result of technology, experience, skill, patience, risk and lots of money. Time beneath the surface is restrictive thus the photographer relies on instinct to capture the subject, to freeze a moment which never may be repeated again. An artist begins their work by sketching their subjects and have the luxury of time to come back again and again to get the composition into perspective before putting paint on canvas.

Most award winning underwater photographers prepare their images just like an art director, starting with a layout, selecting a location with bright gorgonian fans and posing a model in a colourful swimsuit. Still an element of luck is required for conditions to be right - for the two bannerfish to swim in front of the lens as the finger presses on the shutter. Then there are the special breed of photographers who are totally focused, specialising in their chosen field from fishes, nudibranchs or corals to shells. They are the scientific photographers whose pictures are used to identify and document bio-diversity of species. They can be unobtrusively obsessive and will travel half way around the world just to capture the image of a single species of fish which broods live young in the mouth. Competition and scientific photographers have two primary characteristics in common - they shoot a lot and they challenge the elements just to get that perfect shot.

With the underlying objectives of this book, I am able to deviate from strictly selecting identification type images, by using some with stronger aesthetic value. The first secret that I would share with you is that behind every one of these images are many others, some unframed, some not even cut, stashed away in cardboard boxes (much to my wife's continual frustration!). The second, you must have the right tool for the job. Like picking a broader brush for thicker stroke and a finer one for details, I use the Nikon 15mm, 16mm and Sigma 14mm for reefscape pictures and for big animals, generally the Nikon 24mm and 20mm lenses. For the shy ones, a 105mm macro is the tool of the trade, but my favorite is the 60mm 2.8 macro with 1:1 capability. Though I house a couple of F90xs in aluminum housings, the Ikelites remain my favorite - they have all the necessary controls, are affordable and quiescently prevail me from going too deep!

UNDERWATER PICTURES

I choose the films I use like an artist choosing the quality of canvas or board; Velvia and Provia are my favorites for their strong colours and grainless characteristics. Together with stringent chemistry and densitometer control in processing, color filters or colour enhancement during colour separation becomes unnecessary. Strobes are like the colour paints of underwater photography. We use them to put the colours and textures of subjects onto our canvas - the film. There are a various qualities of strobes each giving a different tone or warmth to our pictures. I use the Ikelite 150s, 200s and 50s with the convenience of rechargeable batteries, fast recycling and their board beam angle allowing for minimizing backscatter.

Remember this and remember this well - There is no colour beyond 1.5m, thus get close to your subject. Water is 800 times denser than air, hence using that attribute in an analogy, topside flash photography of a subject 2 meters away, the light needs only to travel a total of 4 meters, but underwater it is an equivalent to 3200m. (this is not exactly correct, but the principle applies). So for pictures that reflect true colours and textures, get as close as possible to the subject. This is one of the golden rules of underwater photography.

There is logic in the saying that if the mountain does not come to Mohammed, Mohammed must go to the mountain. This proverb aptly applies to underwater photography - you must be in the right place at the right time and to do that you must spend a lot of time underwater seeking out the addresses of all your subjects and 'knocking' on their door to get their pictures. Within the content of this book, you may not find a exact house address for them, but I believe we have at least directed you to the approximate suburbs.

A great underwater picture is not made by accident, nor by chance. It requires knowledge, practice, perseverance and patience before 'luck' drops in to make a great picture. Beside each picture, I have shared with you information on the lens used and exact exposure details. Additionally, in each chapter, I have included some suggestions which you might find useful in your photographic sojourn.

Happy Shooting.

Sea Posies
60mm f5.6, 1/60
Kakaban, East Kalimantan

MARINE PLANTS

"Finish your vegetables or you will not leave this table!" Sound familiar? Obviously mother always knows best - those leafy greens are necessary for you to grow strong, healthy and wise. Likewise, marine plants are important for the coral reef. In fact, without them the marine environment and it's ocean life simply would not exist. They are the mothers, the genesis of the ocean, the catalyst of life. They are also often ignored. Many of us turn our backs on them. Being a primary producer, marine plants convert solar energy and generate nutrients of energy-rich organic compounds. Marine plants provide the platform for reefs and nutrition for multitudes of macro-organisms, as well as corals, molluscs, crustaceans and fishes which, in turn, are the food source of larger predators. Marine plants are the beginning of the food chain, the start and the end of the web of life on our water planet. Much of the sea's life spends its juvenile days beneath the fronds of marine plants. Marine plants are characterised into two main types: seaweeds or algae; and sea grasses.

Algae, by far the most abundant, have the most primitive structure of all plants. They are mostly single-celled and lack true leaves, stems and roots. Sea grasses are considered to be higher plants and, similar to many land plants, bearing flowers, fruit and seeds. Sea grass is usually confined to reef flats with suitable substrates for growth. Algae life grows from reef slopes to deeper water, but generally appears in areas having plenty of sunshine.

BROWN ALGAE

The most common tropical forms of brown alga are *Sargassum* and *Turbinaria*, of which there are a number of species. They are easily recognised by round air bladders which help flotation when wave action causes them to break away from their holdfast (the bottom stalk anchoring them to the substrate). After the monsoon season in the tropics, large Sargassum weeds often form huge extensive floating beds and rafts close to shore. These seaweed beds are a nursery for juvenile crabs, shrimps, molluscs and many young fishes. *Sargassum* forests support an entire living community, offering protection and shelter to many free-living animals, while some live attached to the blades, holding fast. Another common brown algae is the *Padina* species which has simple white circular or funnel-shaped fronds.

GREEN ALGAE

Green algae is often seen to cover an extensive area and it is not uncommon to find some reefs literally blanketed with green algae. Green algae is sometimes an indicator of pollution as it thrives in water enriched with organic wastes. While brown algae is restricted to the marine world, green algae is also found in freshwater environments. Common green algae are *Halimeda tuna* and *Halimeda opuntia*, which look like chains of flat-shaped leaves impregnated with calcium carbonate and always attached to the substrate. Sea-grapes, *Caulerpa* species, are also commonly seen in great abundance, living among an assemblage of hard corals.

Funnelweed
Padina gymnospora
60mm / f22 1/60
Bunaken, Nth Sulawesi

Sea grapes
Caulerpa racemosa
105mm / f22 1/60
Bunaken, Nth Sulawesi

Sea grapes & Green algae
Caulerpa racemosa & *Halimeda sp.*
15mm / f5.6 1/60
Nain, Nth Sulawesi

Red Algae

Red coralline algae forms calcareous encrustations on coral rocks and the shells of large gastropods. It contributes immensely to reef building. This cementing platform effect stabilises the substrate for larvae to settle on and helps build up the reef structure. The coating of red algae on rocky surfaces has the appearance of red paint..

Sea Grasses

Submarine plants, otherwise known as sea grasses, grow extensively on coastal reef flats, especially those with a high proportion of fine sediment. These plants have extensive root systems which aid in binding and consolidating the sediment. Sea grasses are like meadows beneath the sea for sea cows (dugongs) and turtles. They are provide a rich habitat for marine organisms and an important nursery ground for shrimps, sea horses and a host of other reef invertebrates. A common species is *Enhalus acoroides* which is often seen in submerged grasslands on remote tropical islands. Sea grass blades are composed of minerals, carbohydrates, proteins and fats.

Mangroves

Mangroves stand by the edge of the reefs. They are trees sustained by sea water. The mangroves are also of extreme importance to the welfare of the coral reef. Mangrove forests are a distinct ecosystem within the reef environment, providing nurseries for a wealth of marine organisms. The ecology of mangrove habitats are too complex to be discussed in this text, but their richness of biological diversity makes exploration an enchanting experience.

Foraminifera

Foraminifera is not a plant, but is, in fact, an important single-celled animal belonging to the *Phylum Sarcomastigophora*. The only reason they are included in this section, is because they are green. Estimation has it that 50% of the Earth's calcareous sedimentary rock formed on sea bottoms originates from the shells of Foraminiferida animals. Like most marine plants, they are common, they are overlooked, and they get little attention. The structure of these animals, commonly known as foram, is simply a blob of green jelly-like protoplasm within a shell of calcium carbonate. Though these animals feed on a variety of microscopic organisms, they harbour a symbiotic algae which manufactures nutrients for them as a food supplement. They are often found attached to hard corals or algae communities over extensive areas, mostly on outer reef slopes. There are also free-living pelagic species that float in the open sea. There are several species of foram, each with its own distinctive shell that is composed of one or more chambers. Dead forams are a vital addition to bottom composition which makes them an important contributor to the reef building process.

Pictures of Marine Plants

Not many photographers have marine plants in their portfolio, yet they are one of the most sought-after images in photo libraries around the world. Sea grass beds and mangrove forests are an ideal studio for "half and half" photography. 16mm and 20mm lens are recommended. Among the green leaves and roots dwell many surprises for the macro photographer.

WHAT IS THAT SHINY ROUND THING?

One solitary life form on the reef yields tremendous curiosity among divers, not because it performs any neat tricks, or because it is big and mean, but perhaps because it looks like a familiar object, resembling the balls of a pinball machine. These shiny round things are single-celled algae, *Valonia ventricosa*, commonly known as Sailor's Eyeball.

105mm / f32 1/125, Tukang Besi, Sulawesi

Mangrove habitat
20mm / f8 , 1/ 60
Kakaban, Kalimantan

Red algae
Peyssonnelia sp.
60mm / f22 , 1/ 60
Cebu, Phillippines

Mangrove habitat & sea grass
Enhalus acoroides
16mm / f4 , 1/ 60
Togian, Sulawesi

SPONGES PHYLUM PORIFERA

Sponges get no respect. Great naturalists like Aristotle and Pliny thought that they were just plants. It was not until an era of overpaid scientists with too much time on their hands actually sat down and stared at these seemingly motionless organisms that it was discovered that they are really quite active beings pumping water through their bodies and capturing food in the process. With this revelation, sponges were finally recognised and declared to be animals. Classified by scientists as the lowest form of animal in evolutionary trees or, rather, the simplest form of all multi-celled animals, sponges are unique. Instead of participating in the race for evolution which led to humankind, they branched off on their own on the "tree of life" some 550 million years ago.

Since nature has deprived sponges of legs, individuals are attached to the bottom and cannot move. There are however some 10,000 species of sponges, 98% of which are marine dwelling and they are found worldwide from Antarctica to the tropical seas. Sponges are born without a brain, have no heart, no central nervous system and no specialised digestive or respiratory organs.

AMORPHOUS CREATURE AND AMAZING TRICKS

Sponges are not lacking in fashion sense - they come in gold, red, brown, drab brown, green, pink, gaudy purple and yellow. Sponges are asymmetrical, amorphous and they come in all shapes and sizes. Some are basket-like, some round, dish-shaped or tubular. They may take the form of a barrel over 1.5m in height or be as thin as one ten-thousandth of an inch thick. Some are just plain weird and knobby; similar to those cocoons in Sigourney Weaver's Alien trilogy series. Sponges are formed either of calcium carbonate, silica or flexible protein fibres called spongin. Scientifically, they are divided into four classes. *Calcarea* are mostly small, coloured white and yellow, with calcium carbonate transparent spicules. *Sclerospongiae* and *Hexactinellida* are supported by glass-like siliceous and are found only in water beyond 90m. *Demospongiae* are those with a skeleton made out of fibrous spongin or siliceous or a mixture of both. About 90% of all sponges belong to this last class.

Sponges perform some amazing tricks. With their simple cell structure, sponges regenerate any lost "limbs". Broken pieces may be reformed and carry on living. In 1907, H.V. Wilson from Beaufort, North Carolina pushed a sponge through a coarse cloth, breaking it into individual cells. Almost at once, the cells began to find each other and started to fuse. Subsequent experiments by other sponge scientists concurred that sponge cells not only reorganise themselves but also have the ability to recognise their own DNA. If two species are broken up, stirred around, and placed in a tank, most often the same two sponges will reform. Now that is a pretty impressive trick for a primitive animal without a brain.

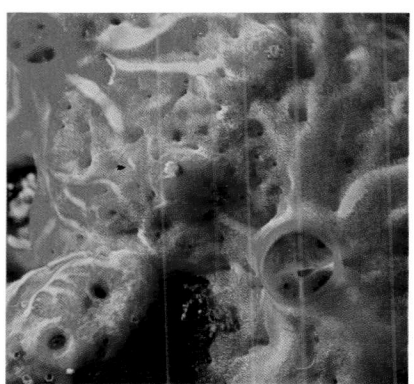

Fire sponge
Clathria mima
105mm / f22 , 1/ 60
Bunaken, Sulawesi

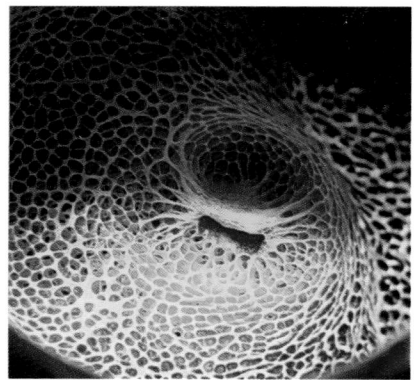

Sponge details
Coelocarteria singaporense
105mm / f32 , 1/ 60
Singapore

Neptune Cup sponge
XietosponaiaClathria mima
15mm / f8 , 1/ 60
Fathers reef, Kimbe Bay, PNG

GREATEST INHALERS

All sponges or *Porifera* are filter feeders. Somewhat restricted in movement, they inhale large quantities of water which is circulated through their porous body to catch food particles. Water is filtered through inhalant pores (ostia), into a chamber via a special cell which contracts to close-off the water system. The flagellated chamber is lined with special cells called choanocytes, which are equipped with microscopic hair-like flagella beating to and fro. All the cells work together to generate a uni-directional current flow, pumping the water through the entire animal, filtering out food as the water passes through the pores.

Sponges grow slowly. It has been estimated that a sponge must filter about one ton of seawater to grow by one ounce (Campbell). Hence, those giant purple barrel sponges which are over two metres in height, and are large enough for a diver to climb inside, could be over one hundred years old. But do not ever be tempted to sit in a sponge. The lip of the sponge is easily broken, which can result in the breakdown of it's pumping action and ultimately seal the fate of the entire colony. Just as it might hurt a one hundred year old person by sitting on them, the act of climbing in or sitting on a giant sponge is practised only by people with a brain smaller than that of a sponge.

WHO WOULD EAT A SPONGE?

Sponges have outlived the dinosaurs. These primitive animals without any obvious way of defending themselves, ie, no legs to run, have survived through the ages and are found in remarkable density throughout virtually every aquatic environment. Be thankful that Saddam "what's his name" is not a sponge. Sponges produce an assortment of foul smelling, diabolic, toxic, noxious chemical compounds. These creatures have been called "chemical warfare plants from Hell". Only a few predators, such as molluscs (sea snails/shells) and echinoderms (sea stars) possess the required taste buds for sponge eating. Eating a sponge must be like biting into an ill-tasting toxic pincushion.

SEX LIFE WITH THE PINCUSHION HOT AND STEAMY

Much like some of us, there are a few species of sponges who lead rather mundane sex lives. These are those which reproduce asexually, either through fragmentation, budding or by producing spores which live on after the parent dies and decomposes. However, most sponges prefer to indulge in a more bisexual method of reproduction. But without the presence of the necessary organs, their procreation exercise is downright bizarre. In some species, individuals are either male or female, but most sponges are hermaphrodites. When it is time to mate, sperm is released like a volcanic eruption into the water column, and currents carry the sperm between mates. When a sperm reaches a receptive partner, it is sucked through the flagellated chamber. In the chamber the sperm penetrates a choanocyte (the special cell) and both cells discard their flagella. In rhythmic amoebic movement (constantly changing as they move), the cells travel to a nearby special egg chamber. After fertilisation, the egg is retained in the body of the sponge, until it develops into a larva, before being spat out through the chamber into the water. These free swimming spirits live out their adolescent stage in the planktonic realm before settling down on the substrate to grow into an adults.

Crimson sponge
Monanchora ungiculata.
60mm / f11, 1/ 60
Komodo Island, Indonesiai

Dish sponge
Ianthella sp.
20mm / f11, 1/ 60
Manado Tua, Sulawesi

Yellow sponge
Leucetta chagosensis
60mm / f16 , 1/ 60
Sangie Island, Nth Sulawesi

Massive sponge
Ianthella sp.
14mm / f5.6 , 1/ 60
Tokian, Sulawesi

Affiliation with Sponges

Sponges are important ecological agents in coral reefs. They overgrow loose material, such as broken shells and other carbonate pieces, and act as a bonding agent for these materials until they become cemented with other encrusting organisms and inorganic materials. Without this encrusting action, loose sand and rubble would be unstable for larvae to settle on and the reef would progressively be eroded into sand. Since ancient times, we have had an intimate relationship with sponges. As early as the bronze age, dried sponge skeletons have been used in baths and sponges have also been used to staunch bleeding.

Since the discovery of one of the only anti-cancer drugs derived from a marine organism was derived from a sponge, marine laboratories and universities are currently seeking chemical compounds from sponges to derive cures for a range of cancers and viruses. So far, agents have been found which kill fungus, bacteria and viruses and some are known to inhibit the growth of cancerous tumors.

A Sponge Revolution

The recent amazing discovery by Jean Vacelet and Nicole Boury-Esnault, of the Oceanic Centre of Marseille, of a new species of sponge has just about rewritten natural history text on sponges. This small sponge is able to catch shrimps and eat them alive. This species belongs to the genus *Asbestopluma*, a deep-water sponge previously known to inhabit depths up to 9,500m. Specimens have also been found in caves between 17/23 m.

The new deadly sponge, named *Asbestopluma hypogea*, eats only the smallest crustaceans. Its body is covered with white whisker-like filaments equipped with miniature claws designed to hook onto shrimp that come within striking range. Once prey is captured, it is drawn close and, as it struggles, it bumps up against more hooks, getting more and more tightly entwined. The filaments then proceed to engulf their dinner though the shrimp may continue to struggle for several hours. Shrimp wouldn't come any fresher to this sponge. Be glad that this sponge grows only to about three quarters of an inch, otherwise we might have headlines that read "Diver Absorbed Alive by Killer Sponge".

How to Shoot a Sponge

Avoid shooting a sponge front on as they tend to appear flat. Being a sponge, they also absorb a lot of strobe power. For macro work, use a powerful, single light source to bring out details. Some shadows accentuate the texture of a sponge. Big sponges are great subjects for pictures of reef perspective, shoot on an upward angle.

Tube sponge
Theonella cylindrica
60mm / f11, 1/ 60
Taka Bonareta, Indonesiai

Pencil sponge
Ciocalypta sp.
60mm / f22, 1/ 60
Siau island Nth Sulawesi

Alien sponge
Stelletinopsis isis
24mm / f11, 1/ 60
Bunaken, Nth Sulawesi

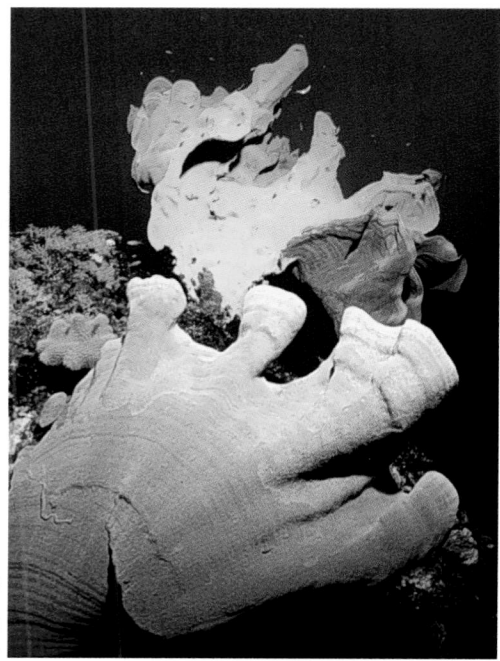

Massive Leafy sponge
Ianthella basta.
20mm / f5.6, 1/ 60
Kimbe Bay, PNG

ARCHERS OF THE CORAL REEF -PHYLUM CNIDARIA

It is not an imaginary creation of Steven Spielberg, or one of J.R.Tolkien's tales, that beneath our oceans there is a fully trained and equipped army of creatures. In this army there are over 10,000 species of animal with a common bond among their rank and file. Each animal is equipped with hundreds and thousands of darts - ready-charged capsules filled with dangerous toxins. These weapons are spring-loaded, attached with a thread that is either sticky or armed with spines. In some advanced species it is a long tube that wraps around its prey. Once activated, it fires off at " the speed of light " to bury deep into the skin of its target, where it explodes, paralysing the prey with deadly toxins. Tentacles then move to shove the neutralised prey into the animal's mouth ... alive. With such an impressive armament, these predators are capable of capturing animals many times their size. Their darts, known as cnidoocil, are the genesis of modern day warfare.

This assemblage of over 10,000 species belongs to the marine phylum *Cnidaria*, which is both the backbone and main frame of a coral reef. This major division in the animal kingdom comprises jellyfish, hydroids, sea anemones, all types of soft and hard corals, gorgonian sea whips and fans. Cnidaria seem to have evolved somewhere in time between the sponges and the worms, having a simplistic yet functional body plan which has been extremely successful in sustaining their existence through the ages.

Their diversity of shape, colour and form, gives both life and aesthetic beauty to the coral reef environment. Species of this phylum inherit no complex organs like brains, heads or hearts, but they possess specialised nerve cells which interconnect and transmit instantaneous pulses in all directions. Their behavior is controlled by this "web" or "nerve net" which produces relatively complex signals, perhaps faster than any modem or fibre-optic cable in your local computer shop. Cnidarians exhibit two distinct body types:
 the medusa form (jellyfish), which is free floating with tentacles pointing down; and
 the polyp type (coral) which is anchored with tentacles pointing upward.

Scientists have divided cnidarians into four separate classes, based on the presence of polyps and medusa. In the *Class Scyphozoa*, composed primarily of jellyfish, the medusa (a thick layer of firm jello) is dominant and polyps are rarely developed. The *Class Cubozo* are cuboidal swimming cups, found in tropical and subtropical water, most of which are about one inch (2-3 cm) in diameter. The *Class Hydrozoa* is characterised by a greater representation of polyps and, in some species, both polyps and medusa are equally prominent. Fire corals, Portuguese Man-of-War and hydroids are all hydrozoans. Finally, the dominant class of cnidarians is the *Anthozoa*, which are distinguished by their pronounced polyps or colonies of polyps formed. Activity on a coral reef focuses heavily on the anthozoans, which comprises all hard corals, soft corals, stony corals, sea anemones, sea whips and gorgonian fans. Generally, all cnidarians are carnivorous, but exceptions do exist.

Ingenious reef building corals have drawn up a living arrangement with single-cell algae - zooxanthellae. These symbionts, or photosynthetic algae, grow on the cnidarian collecting sunlight for energy. The host provides rent-free accommodation and the guests help with food for calcification, enabling the cnidarian to grow at a faster pace.

Though cnidarians are simplistic animals, the importance of their existence and survival to sustain a healthy reef environment cannot be over-emphasised. Without them, there would be no reef.

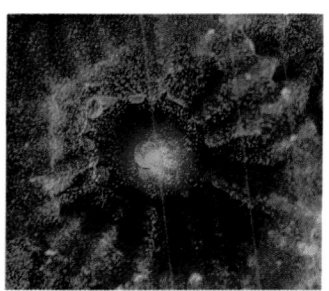

Birth of an egg bundle
from a single coral polyp.
105mm / 16 : 1 magnification

After -birth of the same
coral polyp seen through a
medical boroscope

BURNING HYDROZOANS - PHYLUM CNIDARIA

What burns in paradise without fire? Fire corals, hydroids and the Portuguese Man-of-War are all hydrozoans, otherwise known as pests from hell in paradise. Related to jellyfish and corals in the *Phylum Cnidaria*, hydrozoans are both beautiful and delicate but they are really "wolves in sheep's clothing". Their stinging cells are called nematocysts and are mostly hidden and extremely sensitive. When triggered, thousands of these spring-loaded venomous darts are released at once.

There are about 2,700 species of *Hydrozoa* distributed mostly in tropical waters, including those that are found on the sea's surface, *Velella* and *Physalia*, the Portuguese Man-of-War, floating with it's large sail-like gadgets above water for locomotion and long tentacles below the surface to fish for food.

LEAFY FLAMES

Hydroids are the most common form of hydrozoans on the coral reef. They are the most primitive of the class, consisting of feathery or bushy colonies inhabiting shells, sponges, seaweeds and areas among other sessile animals. Hydroids have caused many a sleepless night to unwary snorkellers and swimmers who have brushed against these seemingly harmless ferns of the sea. Their stings are brutally painful and are known to leave behind perennial scars.

Hydroids spend most their life as polyps, though when they are young they usually go through a short medusa (jellyfish-like) transitional stage. Most hydroid polyps grow in branching sessile colonies, which range in length from a few centimetres to over one metre. Nudibranchs, crabs and shrimps are known to adorn their bodies with tiny hydroid branches as a defence system. I have often wondered if there is a "Mafia of the sea" trading hydroids as armaments

FAMILY AFFAIRS

Hydrozoans have separate polyps, some equipped with nematocysts for defence, some for feeding and other specialised cells for reproduction. These horny cells begin the sexual procreation process by budding to form tiny medusae on the hydrozoan's branches. These wriggly medusae, less than two millimetres long, break off to become free swimming. After procuring either eggs or sperm in the water column, the medusae expire, having fulfilled their parental duties. Fertilised eggs hatch into planulae larvae that eventually settle onto the reef environment and flourish into new branching colonies.

Colour variation of Stimaina hydroids
Agloaphenia cupressina
60mm / f22 , 1/ 60
Halmehera , Indonesia

Sponges, tunicates protected by stinging hydroids
60mm / f16 , 1/ 60
Derawan, East Kalimantan

One of the most unusual or infamous of the hydrozoans that has made headlines is the Portuguese Man-of-War. These floating devils contain several specialised types of polyp. The largest is the balloon-like polyp which keeps the colony afloat on the ocean surface. This gas-filled bag may be as large as 30cm in length. The colony also has long tentacles which hang several metres beneath the float, causing havoc to potential prey. Again there is a division of chores for the polyps. Some capture and paralyse food, some digest and some just perform mundane reproduction chores. Humans that have survived an intimate encounter with this animal describe their experience as being on a trip to hell and back.

Hot Rocks

Fire coral (*Millepora*), which are often mistaken for hard coral, are another form of hydrozoan. They are more closely related to jellyfish than just their colour. They tend to look dead, without any visible tissues, tentacles, polyps or mucus.

There are 48 species of fire coral found worldwide, predominantly on reef crests and in shallow water. Common fire corals are thriving with small branching calcareous growths, but without the defined cups found in true stony coral. All species have a characteristic white edge or tip that serves to warn the unwary "touch me not, I am a hot rock". Other relatives of fire coral are the delicate lace coral (*Stylaster sp.*) and the beautiful purple or orange-coloured *Distichopora* species.

Scientifically, milleporas have distinct specialised polyps: feeding is done by the gastropores, while defence and the capture of prey is done by the mouthless dactylozoids which are equipped with three types of stinging cells. These cells are also used to take over territories occupied by other animals. Milleporas are often seen to completely grow over other sessile animals, particularly gorgonian fans.

Pictures of Flames

Some of my favorite pictures of hydroids are of those which live with colonies of sea squirts (see "Tunicates", p138). They serve as little fronds of "baby's breath" or ferns to the sea posies. A 60mm macro lens or macro extension tubes are essential for both scientific identification and aesthetic images.

Lace hydroid
Gymnangium gracilicaule
60mm / f22 , 1/ 60
Bunaken, Nth Sulawesi

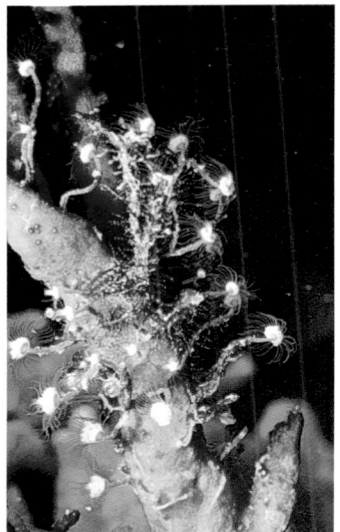

Tubularia sp
60mm / f22 , 1/ 125
Komodo, Indonesia

Plumularia sp.
60mm / f22 , 1/ 60
Davoa, Phillippines

Distichopora - Colour variations.
60mm / f16, 1/ 60
Banka Island, Nth Sulawesi

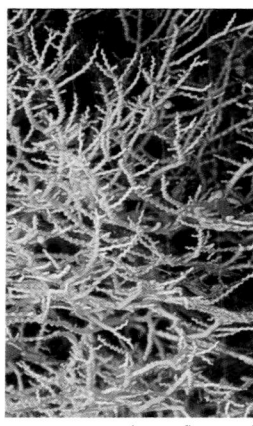

Lace fire coral
Stylaster sp
60mm / f22 , 1/ 125
Batuna Reef, Phillippines

Lace fire coral
Stylaster sp
60mm / f22 , 1/ 60
Bunaken, Nth Sulawesi

Reef edge of *Aglaophenia cupressina*
24mm / f11 , 1/ 60
Manado Tua, Nth Sulawesi

JELLYFISH - PHYLUM CNIDARIA

Vic Hislop and other shark hunters only ever pick fights with sharks, and never jellyfish; perhaps because they know that sharks are less dangerous than jellyfish. In Australia, sea wasps or box jellyfish (*Chironex fleckerii*) have fatally stung over 80 bathers, swimmers and surfers in the last 100 years - some dying within minutes of meeting these Darth Vaders of the ocean. Scientists and doctors have named the jellyfish "Medusa", after the evil Greek monster who had snakes instead of hair, and rightly so. Legend has it that even after Medusa's head was cut off, whoever gazed upon it turned into stone. The tentacles of a jellyfish can cause an agonizing sting, even after they have been separated from their "head", and even when they are out of water. Scientifically jellyfish belong to the *Class Schyphozoa*. There are about 200 species of jellyfish inhabiting the world's oceans from tropical reefs to the Arctic ocean. While most prefer to live in shallow coastal water, some have been found at depths of more than 3,600 m.

JELLYFISH ARE NOT FISH

Jellyfish are in fact close relatives of corals. They are divided into two parts, the bell and tentacles, and are one of the most ancient animals. Composed of 95% water, with a little protein, fat and salt, Medusae are brainless, heartless and earless. Most of them have nothing resembling eyes or gills, but they are able to absorb oxygen directly from water. The jellyfish's bell ranges in shape from a parachute or helmet, to a satellite dish or Frisbee, and contains a mouth and stomach, and often the sex organs and nerves as well. Jellyfish have a mouth, which is also the opening to their body surrounded by tentacles leading to a hollow gut. The number of tentacles ranges from a few to more than 800 in some species. These appendages dangle only 1 cm in some species while others may reach a length of 36m, equivalent to the height of a 10 storey building.

FISHING WITHOUT LINE AND ROD

Most jellyfish hunt by raising and lowering their tentacles in the water column, basically fishing at varied depths. All of their tentacles have stinging cells which are spring-loaded with toxin-filled darts. When a tentacle encounters prey, stinging cells in the vicinity are triggered to fire by a combination of chemical and contact stimulation, discharging hundreds or thousands of spiny darts to paralyse the target. Scientists estimate that a single tentacle of a Box Jellyfish, a jellyfish in Northern Australian waters and possibly other tropical locations, may contain as many as 750,000 stinging cells. A tiny shrimp might cause fifty stinging cells to discharge and a small fish may attract a thousand, but something big like a John or Mary Smith might receive hundreds of thousands of these poisonous needles. Even after death, jellyfish can still be bad news. Beware of touching those motionless blobs that are washed up on the beach after storms or strong swells. The nematocysts on the tentacles are totally independent of the animal's nervous system and they can still fire even when the tentacles have been severed from the bell. Fortunately, stingers of many jellyfish are harmless to human beings due to their lack of penetration power, but quite a few species are capable of delivering excruciatingly painful stings and even death.

Upside down sea jelly
Cassiopeia andromeda
60mm / f16 , 1/ 60
Pulau Puan Malaysia

Lion's mane sea jelly
Cyanea capillata
17mm / f5.6 , 1/ 60
Bahara Rock, Malaysia

Spotted sea jelly
Phyllorhiza punctata
14mm / f8 , 1/ 60
Kakaban, East Kalimantan

JELLYFISH DINERS

Throughout the world's oceans, sea turtles, particularly the Hawksbill and Loggerhead, enjoy a feast of chewy jellyfish as their favourite meal. Fishes too, such as barracuda, cod, mackerel and dogfish love to nibble on the translucent blubber, seemingly unaffected by the stinging cells - they must have pretty tough or thick tongues. Sadly, these days, "swimming" in the world's oceans are many plastic bags disguising themselves as jellyfish. Plastic bags are not biodegradable and have unfortunately been found, and will continue to be found, in the stomachs of many dead marine animals.

JELLYFISH IN MOTION

Jet propulsion is not a new engineering dynamic of the 20th century. For 850 million years jellyfish have been using this technique to propel themselves, expanding and contracting their bells, thus expelling water, to move themselves up and down the water column. Male jellyfish will only release their sperm in groups, in big company, in big masses of as many as one hundred jellyfish per cubic metre of water - the more the merrier. Research by UCLA in Vancouver recorded that jellyfish (Aurelia aurita) which are loosely distributed in the northern fjord in early summer will converge into two dense swarms at the south eastern tip of Vancouver island by September (Marine Biology, Vol 119, pp347-356). They swim parallel to the water surface during daylight, using the sun as a compass to head on their south-easterly course. At night they just swim vertically with their bell facing up or down. Similarly, in Australia, from November to May, millions of Chironex medusae are observed coming into the shallow inshore bay of Adelaide to feed and spawn. How such a simplistic animal without a brain is able to perform such amazing navigational manoeuvres is a mystery to even the most educated human being . The development of baby jellyfish is somewhat intriguing as well, because they go through two completely different life stages. As eggs inside sexually mature female jellyfish are fertilised by sperm, tiny planulae larvae are released into the water. In the spirit of the survival of their species, these little larvae find their way into inshore bodies of water, like mangrove swamps, to settle on the hard bottom. Here they metamorphose into polyp-like "scyphistomae" with long solid tentacles and a short stalk - sort of like a tiny Medusa's head on a stick stuck to the ocean bottom. These cool little heads then spend the winter feeding the contents of their "head" and reproducing asexually by budding off other polyps. When spring comes, the polyps metamorphose into devilish little medusae and head for coastal waters, gradually developing into adults which, come summertime, will begin to form new swarms, hence the circle of life.

SHOOTING JELLYFISH

I love pictures of Medusae, but they can be dangerous to work with, not just because their stings of death can ruin your day. Jellyfish swim near the surface, up and down the first 20 feet. To chase after them on scuba is a game of Russian roulette for air embolism. Try free diving and shoot them with a 20mm lens against the sun. Always aim for the sky when working with jellyfish. The iridescent body pulsating and quivering against an aqua-blue liquid ceiling is a picture worth dying for.

Juvenile trevally
shelter beneath the umbrella
of sea jelly for protection
Cephea sp.
20mm / f11 , 1/ 60
Phi Phi Island, Thailand

Swimming with sea jelly
without wetsuit is a game
of Russian Roulette
Cephea sp.
20mm / f11 , 1/ 60
Alor, Indonesia

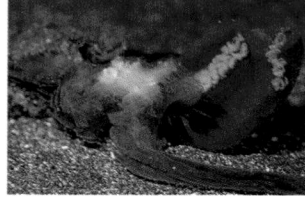

This one had just suffered
injury from a sea turtle
Unidentified species.
(Order Rhizostomeae)
60mm / f11 , 1/ 60
Kelasey, Nth Sulawesi

The most common
upside-down sea jelly
found in the
marine lake in Kakaban
Cassiopea sp.
60mm / f11 , 1/ 60
Kakaban, East Kalimantan

SEA ANEMONE - PHYLUM CNIDARIA
CLASS ANTHOZOA, ORDER ACTINARIA

The sea anemone, though resembling a harmless terrestrial flower, possesses deceptively delicate, wavering tentacles which are equipped with powerful stinging cells known as nematocysts. A close relative of reef-building hard coral, anemones are members of the *Class Anthozoa* within the *Cnidaria Phylum*. An anemone is similar to an overgrown, oversized coral polyp stripped of its hard calcareous skeleton.

A wide variety of anemones are found on tropical reefs; living beneath caverns, wrecks, coral crevices and sand bottoms. Some will even set up home on the backs of crustaceans, but the most conspicuous species are those which play host to clownfish. The tenant/landlord relationship between the clownfish and the anemone is one of the most successful symbiotic arrangements in the sea (Michael AW's *Tropical Reef Fishes, A Marine Awareness Guide*, pp 84-86).

THE BASICS OF THE SEA ANEMONE

A sea anemone is really a hollow tube of muscular tissue with a closed end attached to a rock or any suitable hard surface though not all are stalked. The hollow centre contains numerous walled partitions which act as the digestive area and as devices for respiration and excretion. The top of the hollow tube or column is crowned with tentacles. These tentacles may be short with tiny clusters of balls, or long with rounded or fine ends; sometimes with colour-tinted tips. The number of tentacles varies between species, but in every case they surround the mouth on an oral disc and serve as food-gathering fronds.

The side of the anemone's cylindrical body has been described as being "as smooth as a baby's bottom". In some anemones, however, the body is covered with wart-like bumps or pimples. This helps scientists to distinguish between species. At the bottom end of business is the pedal disc which acts like a suction pad that can rigidly attach itself to rocks or dead corals, even when they may be buried beneath sand.

Some species of anemone have stinging cells or nematocysts distributed over their entire body surface, although usually they are concentrated on the tentacles. The stinging darts, which may feel sticky to the touch in some species, are used both for self defense and for capturing food. The sea anemone usually feeds on microscopic plants and animals, the most important food source probably coming from the zooxanthellae, although some bigger species will feed on tiny fishes. Like the jellyfish, once the prey is paralysed, the tentacles push the food into the anemone's mouth. The waving fronds and stinging cells are also the anemone's means of deterring predators, such as an inquisitive wrasse, from coming close by.

Colonial anemone
Amphianthus sp.
105mm / f32 , 1/ 60
Labuan, Malaysia

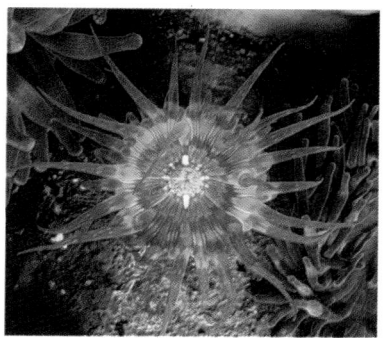

Night anemone
possibly Boloceroides sp.
60mm / f22, 1/ 60
Alor, Indonesia

Orangeball anemone
possibly Pseudocorynactis sp.
105mm / f32, 1/ 60
Kelasey, Nth Sulawesi

Massive manifica anemone,
'castle' of the clownfishes.
Heteractis magnifica
20mm / f5.6 , 1/ 60
Layang Layang, Malaysia

LIVING TOGETHER

Akin to hard coral, most anemones harbour a special ally in their tentacles and column - the algae, zooxanthellae. This photosynthetic algae uses sunlight and carbon dioxide to produce high-energy sugars and amino acids which it shares with its host. Both are important nutritional supplements for the dexterity of the anemone, which is reputed to have a long life span. Like their hard coral relatives, most large anemones attain maximum growth in shallow sun-lit water.

Besides clownfish and algae, the anemone also plays big brother to quite a few species of crustacean. Shrimps and small crabs are often found hiding from their predators by living among the forest of waving toxic tentacles without getting stung themselves (see "Tenancy agreements", p144).

Stephen Spotte of the Mystic Marinelife Aquarium in Connecticut has found that the activity of photosynthesis by zooxanthellae is greatly enhanced with an increased supply of nitrogen, something which is often in short supply in water. The addition of nitrogen, say, in the form of ammonia, has repeatedly been shown to increase production by zooxanthellae. Nearly all marine animals excrete ammonia, including the shrimps, clownfish and crabs that hover tirelessly on or above anemones. Spotte's test documented that shrimps have a marked impact on ammonia levels in the water around the tentacles of the giant Caribbean sea anemone (*Condylactis gigantea*). This added ammonia acts as a fertiliser for the algae to produce more nourishment both for themselves and the anemone. Anemones are known to be territorial and capable of literally "fighting" for their territory with an exchange of swinging tentacles and firing darts. Most anemones are found to be in a solitary existence but at one unique site in Alor, Indonesia, an entire reef slope extending over hundreds of metres is completely layered with several species of anemone.

MORE COUSINS, UNCLES AND AUNTIES

Close cousins of the sea anemone are zoanthids (Order *Zoanthidae, Subclass Zoantharia*), which are small anemone-like animals, usually less than 20mm in diameter. A few zoanthids are solitary, though most are colonial, having the ability to incorporate bottom sediment into a common membranous mat, or mesogloea, as they grow, giving them added support and protection. Almost only tropical, zoanthids reproduce asexually or may spawn in similar fashion to their bigger cousins. Besides having stinging tentacles and toxic flesh, some have sharpened needle-like spicules of calcium carbonate distributed over their tissue for defense.

The order *Corallimorpharia* or Corallimorpharians are anemone-like. Very similar to hard coral anatomically they also lack the calcareous skeleton. They are mainly solitary animals but are still fond of grouping together in huge densities and may carpet extensive sections of reef. Corallimorpharians are bad news as some stings are extremely painful to humans. A friend of ours landed his knee on a huge patch in PNG - the burns and pain he suffered are something he is unlikely to forget for the rest of his life! The *Amplexidiscus fenestrafer* is the largest known species.

Night Jewel anemone (rare)
Alicia rhadina
105mm / f16 , 1/ 60
Derawan, East Kalimantan

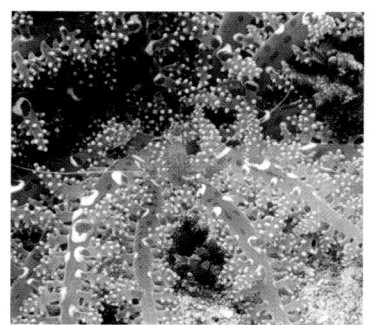

Branching anemone
Actinodendron sp.
60mm / f22, 1/ 60
Alor, Indonesia

Anemone Country
varied species
20mm / f5.6, 1/ 60
Alor, Indonesia

SYNCHRONISED CLIMAX

Anemones are separately sexed, meaning that there are boy and girl anemones. Though the anemone can multiply by budding, nature has dictated that they should practise sexual reproduction as well. As sessile animals that don't always live next to each other, fertilization is impossible without proper synchronisation. Like coral, their amazing nights of sex in the sea are timed for some time after a full moon, only one night each year (see "Coral spawning", p 58).

Eggs and swimming sperm find each other in open water, openly shouting at each other, "Hey let's mate, I am free, I am unattached!" and planulae are born from these fertilised eggs. Not much is known about the early life of a juvenile anemone. It is certain that not many mature to young adulthood, evidenced by the relative rarity of anemones on the reef compared with the 1000's of eggs released. It is also difficult to judge the age of an anemone - even young ones can be quite large because of their ability to expand.

Once a suitable piece of "real estate" is found by a young larvae for it to attach itself to, it will rarely move house, even though an anemone is capable of moving by a slow, sliding-type motion with its pedal disc. Large anemones, such as the *Heteractis magnifica*, are capable of attaining a life span of over 100 years, while Australia's rocky shore species of *Actinia tenebrosa* has an average life span of 50 years and may live to be more than 200 years old. The anemone's longevity combined with it's relatively low survival rate to the reproductive age are two important reasons why the collection of anemones for the aquarium trade should be banned from every reef system.

POPULAR MODEL

The sea anemone is one of the most photographed subjects on the coral reef - actually the clownfish is, but the anemone just happens to be its home. As anemones are bottom dwellers, most photographers tend to shoot them at a downward angle. Try shooting them at eye level with powerful strobes to highlight their tentacles against a blue or black liquid background. Their cylindrical column also makes interesting texture images.

Sand anemone
Condylactis sp.
60mm / f16 , 1/ 60
Kelasey, Nth Sulawesi

Sand anemone
Actinodendronidae megalactus
60mm / f22, 1/ 60
Bali, Indonesia

Corallimorphorian
Rhodactis sp.
60mm / f22, 1/ 60
Siau, Nth Sulawesi

Manifica anemone
Heteractis magnifica
20mm / f11, 1/ 60
Kimbe Bay, PNG

Hard Coral - Scleractinia PHYLUM CNIDARIA

Nearly half a billion years ago, before there was any life on land, there lived in the sea primitive coral. This coral bore a very close resemblance to the corals alive today. Modern corals evolved at about the time of the dinosaurs (200 million years ago), filling the ecological niche left empty by the extinction of hard corals of the tabulate and rugose species. Millions upon millions of tiny hard coral polyps make up the superstructure of a reef, forming the underwater equivalent of a modern metropolis - like the great cities of the world, New York, Tokyo and Hong Kong - with its own hotels, serviced apartments, condominiums, units, townhouses and warehouses of the ocean.

An estimated 500-600 species of reef-building corals are found in the Indo-Pacific region; 10 times more than the number of species found in the Caribbean, or up to 75% more genera and 85% more species of coral than are found in Eastern Pacific waters (Wilkinson, 1987). These corals secrete calcareous limestone, deposited over generation after generation of coral polyps, forming the platform or foundation of today's coral reefs. Scleractinia hard coral are the architects, builders, plasterers, and brick layers, providing homes and offices, rent-free, to hundreds, thousands and millions of the reef's animals. Apart from the forms and aesthetic quality of stony hard corals, their function is much more than just skin-deep. They are the soul, the life blood, the pulse, the provider of life on the coral reef, providing habitats, food, protection and shelter. Some hard corals form into extensive table-like colonies while others grow into large boulders, such as the brain coral. Polyp sizes range from less than tenth of a centimeter in some species, to as large as 25cm in the case of the solitary single-polyp mushroom coral.

There are two main types of hard coral - zooxanthellate and azooxanthellate - that is, those which contain a concentration of single-celled algae, zooxanthellae, within their tissues and those which don't.

The ABCs of Hard Coral

Hard coral is simply a thin layer of living tissue overlying a hard skeleton. Each coral individual or polyp has a fleshy sack topped with a crown of tentacles surrounding the central mouth opening. Like all members of the *Cnidarian Phylum*, there are nematocysts on the tentacles which are used for self defense, as well as to trap and move food to the mouth.

Hard coral sits in a skeletal case, called a corallite, which is secreted by the polyps. Members of a colony are on a network - linked by nature's modem to share a free flow of information and nutrients. For example, during feeding time, when all the tentacles are extended to trap food in the current, should one polyp sense danger it will retract its tentacles and the rest will follow almost instantaneously. There might just be Telecom Coral or the AT&T Coral providing the service.

Staghorn corals
mainly Acropora sp.
16mm / f8 , 1/ 60
Temple of Doom, Great Barrier Reef, Australia

ZOOXANTHELLATE

Reef-building hard corals have a close relationship with zooxanthellae. They harbour these lonesome (unicellular) photosynthetic algae inside their tissues, which gives them a varied range of colours from brown or green to orange. Hermatypic corals are found living mainly in areas where their symbiotic friends are exposed to the sunlight required for photosynthesis activity. Using the sun's energy, the zooxanthellae convert carbon dioxide and water into oxygen and carbohydrates which the coral uses as probably its primary food source. Nitrogen and phosphorous are cycled between the zooxanthellae and the coral polyps. The zooxanthellae take in ammonia given off as waste by the polyps and regenerates it as amino acids. In this way, the zooxanthellae enhances calcification enabling the reef to build at a pace faster than it can be eroded away by physical forces, or eaten away by other animals on the reef although possibly still not fast enough to counteract human disturbance. The most obvious reef-building corals belong to the *Genus Acropora*. These corals form giant tables and staghorn forests on shallow reefs. Though the *Acropora* corals are most prolific in shallow reefs, some do dwell on reef slopes and walls. A few species incorporate UV absorbing pigments in their tissues which give off an eerie glow under ultraviolet light.

AZOOXANTHELLATE CORAL - THOSE WHO LIVE ALONE.

Not requiring sunlight for growth, azooxanthellate are found in deeper water, under ledges, crevices and on deep oceanic walls where the sun seldom reaches. Without solar power, they are smaller and seldom develop into large colonies. The most prominent species, *Tubastrea aurea*, is one of the brightest corals of the reef, found in glowing orange and pink panther pink!

CORAL'S DEFENCE SYSTEM - NEMATOCYST'S POWER

A nematocyst is a double-walled structure comprised of a spirally spring-loaded venom sac, filled with thread, and a minute barb (cnidocil) as a tip. A tiny sensor is positioned just at the rim of the nematocyst. When the sensor is stimulated physically or chemically the capsule explodes to launch the thread with considerable force and speed. The barb penetrates the victim's skin and injects potent venom to paralyse the prey.

NIGHT SNACKS

Hard corals are nocturnal feeders. Besides receiving nutrition supplied by their zooxanthellae, after sunset, the corals extend their tentacles to trap food in the evening currents. If you were a tiny organic being, corals would be your greatest nightmare. Besides the killer nematocyst, some corals secrete traps of sticky film and mobile filaments originating from their stomach cavity to capture larger food particles.

MARXISM, MAO TSE TUNG AND FOUL MOUTHS

All colonial corals are communists! For example, if a polyp member of a plate coral is able to harvest more fish or shrimp, he must share them with the others in the colony. The stomach cavities of colonial coral polyps are interconnected enabling food to be shared among all of the polyps in the colony.

Massive Lettuce coral
Montipora tuberculosa.
14mm / f5.6, 1/ 60
Mahahetang (U/W volcano site), Nth. Sulawesi

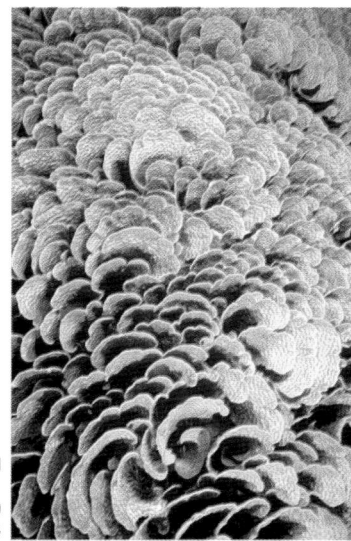

Lettuce coral
Montipora sp.
20mm / f8, 1/ 60
Walindi, PNG

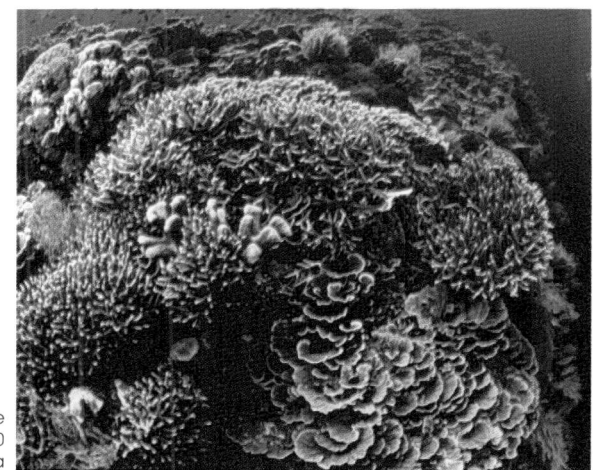

Hard corals assemblage
20mm / f5.6, 1/ 60
Layang Layang, Malaysia

ACROPORA CORALS
BACKBONE OF THE CORAL REEF

Staghorn coral
Acropora formosa
24mm / f8, 1/ 60
Great Barrier Reef, Austrtaliai

Staghorn coral - huge colony
Acropora formosa
20mm / f5.6, 1/ 60
Nain Island, Nth Sulawesi

Staghorn coral - huge colony
Acropora grandis
14mm / f5.6, 1/ 60
Togian, Sulawesi

Staghorn coral
Acropora hoeksemai
20mm / f8, 1/ 125
Komodo, Indonesia

Staghorn coral
Acropora carduus
60mm / f11, 1/ 60
Derawan, East Kalimantan

Staghorn coral
Acropora solitanyensis
20mm / f8, 1/ 60
Togian, Nth Sulawesi

ACROPORA CORALS
BACKBONE OF THE CORAL REEF

Staghorn coral
Acropora formosa
24mm / f8, 1/ 60
Great Barrier Reef, Australia

Staghorn coral - huge colony
Acropora formosa
20mm / f5.6, 1/ 60
Nain Island, Nth Sulawesi

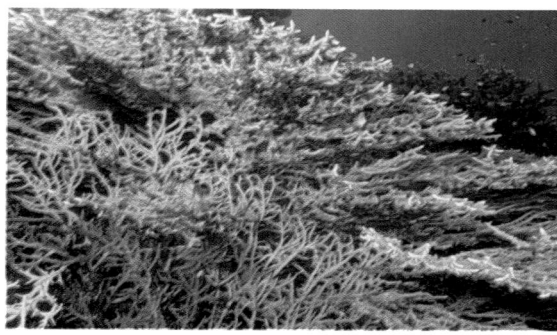

Staghorn coral - huge colony
Acropora grandis
14mm / f5.6, 1/ 60
Togian, Sulawesi

Staghorn coral
Acropora gemmifera
24mm / f8, 1/ 125
Togian, Sulawesi

Staghorn coral
Acropora ovborescents
20mm / f5.6, 1/ 60
Kahahetang, Nth Sulawesi

Staghorn coral
Acropora gemmifera
60mm / f5.6, 1/ 60
Togian, Nth Sulawesi

ACROPORA CORALS
BACKBONE OF THE CORAL REEF

Staghorn coral
Acropora nusata
60mm / f11, 1/ 60
Great Barrier Reef, Australia

Staghorn coral
Acropora valida
60mm / f16, 1/ 60
Annambas, Indonesia

Staghorn coral
Acropora tenuis
60mm / f11, 1/ 60
Bunaken, Nth Sulawesi

Knobby coral
Diplaastrea heliopora
60mm / f11, 1/ 60
Tukang Besi, Indonesia

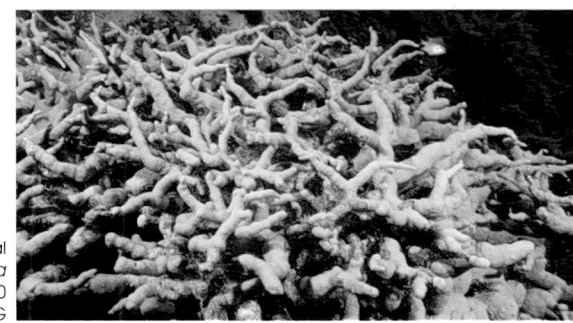

Digitate coral
Porites cylindrica
60mm / f116, 1/ 60
PNG

Massive coral assemblage
Echinopora (background)
P. cylindrica (foreground)
20mm / f5.6, 1/ 60
Togian, Nth Sulawesi

Shapes and Forms of Hard Coral

Most divers give hard corals little attention - to the unappreciative, they are just hard lumps in the ocean. However, scleractinian corals are sculptures, works of art in Planet Earth's underwater galleries. The shapes, the forms, the depths are the product of nature's finest architects and artisans. A hard coral can also be described as a "vase covered with flowers".

Prominent Hard "Sculptures"

The Brancher (branched formation) -
Porites cylindrica, Tubastraea micrantha
Acropora formosa, Acropora lovelli
Pocillopora damicornis
Seriatopora hystrix

The Boulder (massive) -
Symphyllia recta
Favia stelligera, Platygyra daedalea
Porites lutea,

The Tables/Laminates -
Echinopora lamellosa, Acropora tenuis
Acropora cytherea, Acropora hyacinthus

The Free Spirits (free living) -
Fungia sp. (all mushroom coral)
Heliofungia actiniformis

The Folioceous (leafy) -
Turbinaria sp. , Pavona cactus
Montipora aequituberculata,

The Least Photographed Model

Hard corals are among some of the best underwater models - they are the Cindys and Elles of the ocean. They have great variations in figure, they pose well and they don't run away from the photographer. However, they are the least photographed. Take the challenge, hard corals make a great shot. Use the widest angle lens possible (13mm, 16mm). For individual portraits of a colony a 28mm or 35mm lens works best.

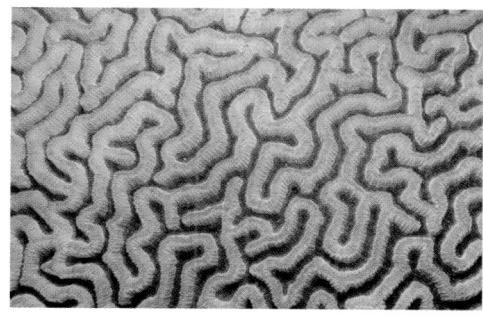

Brain coral
Platygyra lamellina
60mm / f22, 1/ 60
Pulau Aur, Malaysia

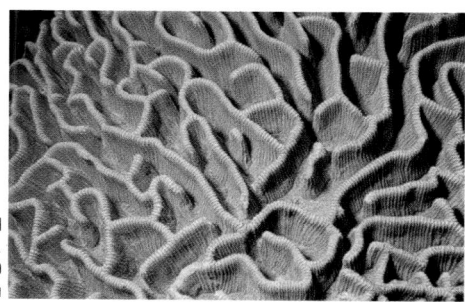

Ridge coral
Oulophyllia sp.
60mm / f11, 1/ 60
Great Barrier Reef, Australia

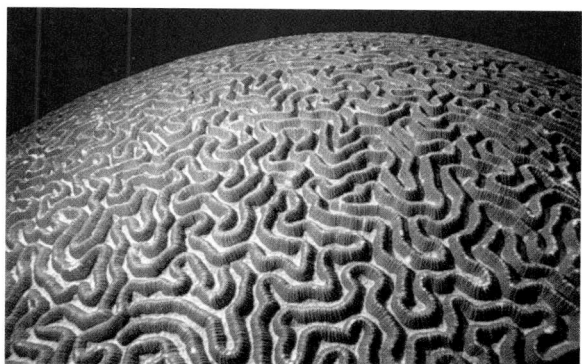

Brain coral
Goniastrea sp.
14mm / f11, 1/ 60
Biaro Islland Nth Sulawesi

OTHER REEF BUILDERS

Porites sp.
20mm / f11, 1/ 60
Swain Reef, Australia

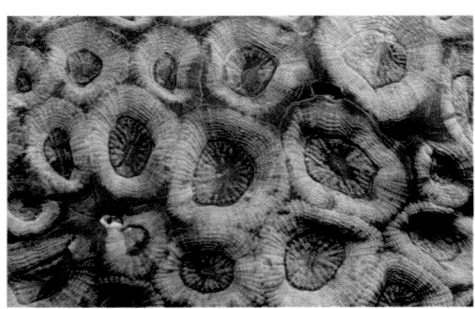

Favia coral
Favia notundata
60mm / f16, 1/ 60
Nain, Nth . Sulawesi

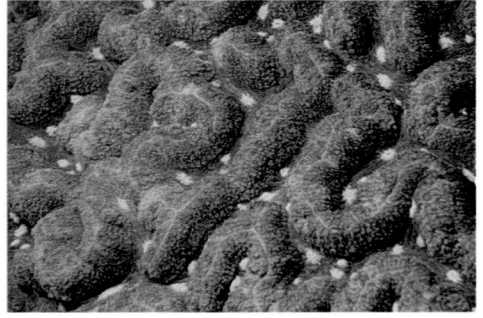

Ridge coral
Lobophyllia sp.
60mm / f11, 1/ 60
Biaro, Nth Sulawesi

MUSHROOM
CORAL

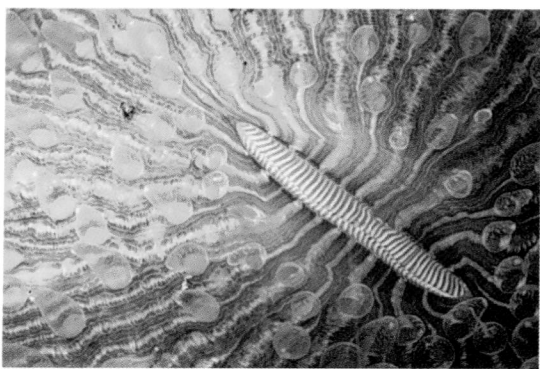

Mushroom coral with
polyps extended.
Fungia sp.
60mm / f16, 1/ 125
Kelasey, Nth Sulawesi

Mushroom coral, possibly
moves together by
strong waves.
Fungia sp.
20mm / f8, 1/ 60
Nain, Nth Sulawesi

Halomitra sp.
24mm / f8, 1/ 60
Walindi, PNG

Non Reef building Hard coral

Colony of *Tubastraea faullkneri* and close- up view.
24mm / 11 1/ 60 & 20mm / f22 1 / 125
Bunaken, Nth Sulawesi

Tubastraea coral colony in the day
with tentacles retracted.
24mm / f8, 1/ 60
Banka Island, Nth Sulawesi

Cynarina lacrymalis.
60mm / f22, 1/ 60
Maldives

Cyathoceras sp.
60mm / f22, 1/ 60
Tukang Besi, Indonesia

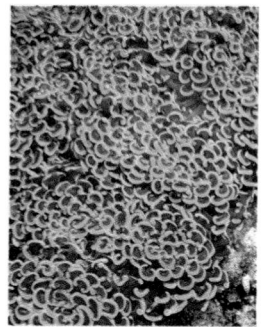

Bubble coral
Euphyllia ancora.
60mm / f16, 1/ 125
Kalabi, Indonesia

Plerogyra sinuosa
60mm / f22, 1/ 60
Alor, Indonesia

Seriatopara hystrix
60mm / f16, 1/ 60
Palawan, Phillippines

Nature's Greatest Night of Orgy

Strange as it may seem it is not unusual for corals to possess both male and female reproductive cells - scientifically known as hermaphrodites. Both sexes can be found in a single colony or a colony may be comprised of only males or females.

The development of a coral colony is achieved by a method of asexual reproduction. Living polyps simply divide or bud to form a complete new polyp which results in the relatively rapid growth of a colony. In some *Acropora* species, a 15cm per year extension to their branching tip has been recorded. Broader colonies, such as brain corals, are much slower growing species. Environmental disturbances, whether natural or man induced, may dislodge some polyps or portions of colonies, and deposit them on another part of the reef. The coral pieces settle and will eventually grow into a new colony.

In addition to this asexual reproductive activity, once a year (or twice on some reefs) after the full moon, nature has synchronised coral to reproduce sexually in a mass spawning activity to increase the success of fertilisation. This unique phenomenon was first observed and studied on Australia's Great Barrier Reef by Dr. Carden Wallace and her colleagues.

Looking at the big picture, on the 2,500 major reef complexes of the Great Barrier Reef are found approximately 350 species of hard coral. On each reef there may be millions of colonies, and in each colony uncountable numbers of coral polyps live together. They might co-habitate, sharing the same high-rise apartments, but they are as independent of each other as a man and women in the same household. But the amazing thing is, each year four to five nights after the November full moon, the entire coral community, one species after another, explodes its sperm and eggs into the water column after sunset: the sea literally smells of sex, a sea of love. While sperm chase after eggs to fertilise, nocturnal creatures feast endlessly, celebrating the new season of the sea.

The question is, among so many individuals, who initiates this behaviour, and how is the cue given? Is there a sort of governmental body that decides the sequence in which each species will spawn after sundown (imagine a particular colony being issued with a ticket for ejaculating prematurely), or do the chiefs of the species come together for a meeting to determine the agenda and bid for the order to release their eggs and sperm?

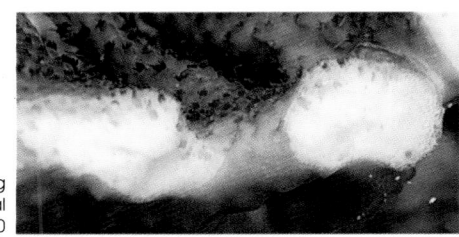

Eggs, one month before spawning
Staghorn coral
60mm / f16, 1/ 60

Setting of egg bundles,
just before release.
60mm / f11, 1/ 60
Magnetic Island, Australia

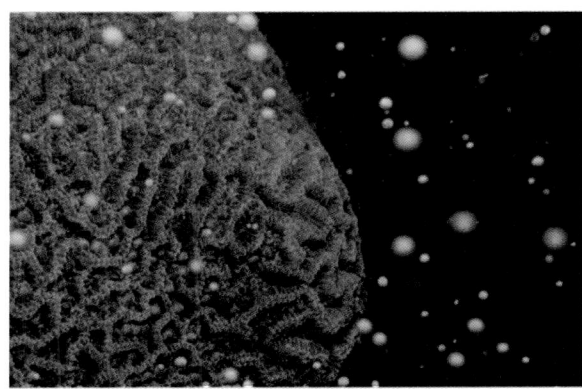

Synchronised release of
egg and sperms bundles.
Goniastrea sp.
24mm / f11 , 1/ 60
Magnetic Island, Australia

Nature's Greatest Night of Orgy

The success of synchronised spawning depends on exact timing for release of both sperm and eggs, but how did coral evolve to achieve such precise synchronisation of their body clocks? Another factor which is really amazing is that sperm and eggs of the same colony do not fertilise each other. Eggs are able to reject sperm which have originated from their own colony, but will readily accept a sperm mate from a different colony but of the same species.

Successful mating takes place when the head of a sperm penetrates an egg, jettisons his tail, and within a few hours the egg develops into a swimming larva called a planula. The little bullet-shaped larva rides on the planktonic layer of the sea to build another colony elsewhere on a coral reef. Once settled, it metamorphoses into a single coral polyp, and the development of a mouth surrounded by tentacles ensues. The new single polyp then begins the colony building process by asexual multiplication of polyps, and a new empire of hundreds to thousands of individuals will eventually evolve.

Imagine those huge table-sized plate colonies beginning life from the settlement on a hard surface of just one minute larva called a planula born from the union of a male and female cell (sperm and egg).

Synchronised coral spawning as discovered by Dr. Carden Wallace and friends has provided scientists all over the world with a better understanding of the process by which the ecology of the coral reef is organised. This has helped in the organisation of monitoring programs to improve the health and care of coral reefs, resulting in reports of corals in Micronesia spawning in June/July, and in Exmouth, Western Australia in March/April. To replenish the loss of coral both from natural and man-made causes, this annual reproduction process is vital to the survival of a reef system. Successful fertilisation is easily affected by freshwater run-off and, according to Dr. Robert Richmond of the University of Guam marine laboratory, a 15% drop in sea water salinity can cause a nearly 90% drop in the coral fertilisation rate.

SEX IN THE SEA PICTURES

Patience is of the essence when it comes to capturing images of the coral spawning event. By their biological clock, eggs and sperm are drawn together into bundles and pushed towards the mouth of each polyp, creating a tiny coloured bulge beneath the transparent tissue. This is referred to as "setting". From the time of setting to when the bundles actually ooze out into the water can be anything from five minutes to 40 minutes. The shot is worth waiting for but don't turn your back or it will go off the very moment you glance away.

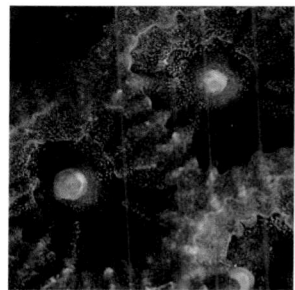

CLOSE - UP VIEW
RELEASE OF SPERM & EGG BUNDLE.
105mm 8 x magnification

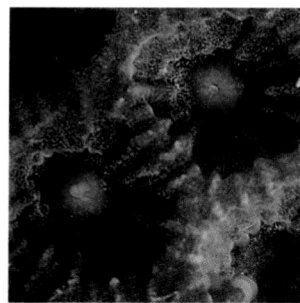

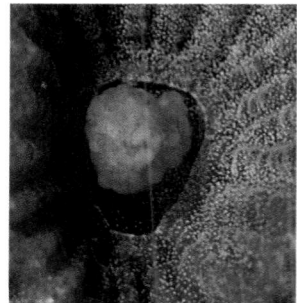

Eggs and sperms separating
as they head towards the surface.
105mm 16 x magnification
Magnetic Island, Australia

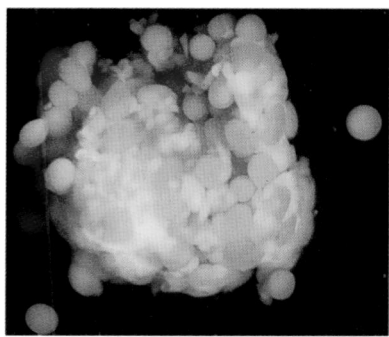

SOFT CORAL PHYLUM CNIDARIA

Exuberant, luscious, kaleidoscopic, elegant and indulgent are a few adjectives associated with soft corals. Some are like wildflowers in bloom, others are fields of golden wheat, the dream of Van Gogh, and there are cherry trees of red, pink, orange, purple and white as well as variegated Christmas trees. If hard corals are the sculptures, soft corals are oils on the canvases of the underwater galleries.

Soft coral, akin to all cnidarians are found in all reef habitats, from shallow reef flats to depths of 60m on abyssal walls. The most gorgeous and prominent are those of the *Dendronephthya* species which are like candy on a tree. They are often found in small congregations beneath table corals, cavern edges, reef walls and slopes where there is constant water movement. On the outer reef of the Australian Coral Sea, yellow specimens up to 3m in height are commonly found beneath coral heads. In the heartland of bio-diversity, Indonesia, Malaysia, PNG, the Philippines and Northern Australia it is not uncommon to find forests of tall sea fans and gardens of red sea whips on the steep reef slopes and walls.

SOFT, SLIMY, FLEXIBLE, BUT WELL CONNECTED.

Soft corals mainly belonging to the subclass of *Alcyonaria* are also known as Octocorals. They are distinguished by the presence of eight tentacles or multiples of eight, as compared to the six tentacles or multiples of six found in hard corals. Tentacles of soft corals are also easily distinguished by rows of very obvious lateral projections or pinnules along each side.

Octocorals are structurally similar to hard coral but lack the support of a hard limestone skeleton. In place of a skeleton is a stem comprised of fleshy tissue and a reinforcement comprised of complex calcareous particles (sclerites) which are similar to those found in sponges.

Species that live on the shallow reef can drastically alter their appearance at various times of the day, depending on whether their polyps are retracted or extended. Their leather-like tissue may expand, contract or wrinkle, for example contracting when exposed at low tide. Sea fans and sea whips have a sort of horny but flexible, continuous internal skeleton which supports the colony of polyps above the substratum enabling them to reach for food in the water column.

Soft corals hunt for food with their nematocysts, packed with poisonous stinging tips and specialised tissue (coenchyme) that connects and distributes food throughout the colony. During feeding time, the polyps outstretch their tentacles in unison to form a living net to capture minute animals and any organic debris. Soft corals are known to be carnivores. However, of late, coral specialists have identified a few vegetarians.

Some of the richest diversity of soft coral in the tropical sea
Layang Layang atoll, Malaysia / 20mm / f5.6 , 1/ 60

Sun Tanning for Power!

Animals of the shallow reef enjoy maximum sun power for photosynthesis. Soft coral species on reef flats like Waving Hands (*Xenia sp.*), alias Pulsing Xenia, and Neon Green Tree Coral (*Nepthea sp.*) harbour the zooxanthellae algae to benefit from the photosynthetic process which manufactures a rich sugar supplement. The zooxanthellae also liven up their host with a range of colours from yellow, green to golden tan. Some shallow dwelling sea whips and fans also adopt zooxanthellae on their outer coating.

Unpleasant Prickles but Wonder Animals

Alcyonarians are known to produce toxic chemicals to fend off other encrusting animal which may wish to grow on them. It also serves as a deterrent to predators trying to take a bite of these juicy, soft, fleshy animals. Even if the predators are immune to the toxin most soft corals have a large number of sclerites or spicules distributed throughout the bodies. These minute structures are formed from calcium carbonate shaped into sharp needles with pointed tips. Eating a soft coral is like biting on a watermelon of needle and pins! Though soft corals are safe from most animals some specialised cowries and nudibranchs eat and live on soft corals and sea fans.

Since the bodies of soft corals are freed from encrusting animals by their chemical secretions, they are the target of many medical researchers for wonder drugs which may inhibit cancerous growths and other human diseases.

Making Softies!

Soft corals are separately sexed. This means that there are male and female gorgonian fans, male and female sea whips and so forth. Sexual reproduction is attained by releasing eggs and sperm into the water. Timing is of the essence for maximum fertilisation and perpetuation of their species (see hard coral's reproduction). Some protective females retain their eggs, and hope for swimming sperms to land on them, to increase their chances of successful reproduction.

Fertilised eggs hatch into larvae to wander through the planktonic layer for a brief period Thereafter, surviving larvae must settle down to mature. Vacant property on a coral reef is scarce. Mortality rates are high. Few survive to find a suitable plot. Successful larvae metamorphose into anemone-like polyps to sprout another, and another and another This budding process continues and, in time, a new colony is formed.

Identification of soft corals is extremely difficult. Among coral experts of the world relatively little research has been conducted on soft corals. Some families are in desperate need of reclassification. Identification of many species is virtually impossible.

Mushroom leather coral blossom
in deeper reef.
Sarcophyton sp
14 mm / f8 , 1/ 60
Fathers reef, Kimbe bay, PNG

Lavish soft coral coverage on off shore oil rig.
Dendronephthya sp
16 mm / f5.6, 1/ 60
Bontang, Kalimantan, Indonesia

Soft coral covered cavern.
ronephthya and varied sp
24 mm / f8, 1/ 60
Maldives

TYPES OF SOFT CORALS

Tree Ferns or Flower Soft Corals
  Xenia sp.
  Nepthea sp.
  Clavularia sp.

Leathery Soft Coral
  Lobophytum sp.
  Sarcophyton sp

Soft Tree or Scrub Corals
  Dendronephthya sp.
  Lemnalia sp.

Sea Fans
  Subergorgia sp.
  Semperina sp.
  Acabaria sp.
  Acalycigorgia sp.

Sea Whips
  Ctenocella sp.
  Junceella sp.

Sea Pens
  Veretillum sp.
  Virgularia sp.
  Pteroeides sp.

Gorgonian fan
Semperina sp.
20mm / f8 , 1/ 60
Manado Tua, Nth Sulawesi

Dendronephythya sp
24mm / f8 1/ 60
Semilan, Thailand

Sea pen
Pteroeides sp.
60mm / f11 , 1/ 60
Mabul, Malaysiai

Leathery soft coral
Sinularia sp
20mm / f11 , 1/ 60
Manado Tua, Nth Sulawesi

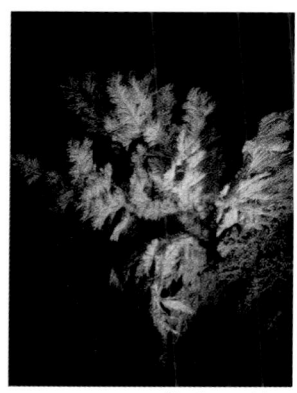

Black coral tree
Antipathes sp.
20mm / f5.6 1/ 60
Mahahetang, Nth Sulawesi

Whip coral
Ellisella sp.Sinularia sp
20mm / f5.6 1/ 60
Walijndi PNG

Sea pen
Pteroeides sp.
60mm / f11, 1/ 60
Kelasey, Nth Sulawesi

Pen soft coral
Veretillum sp.
60mm / f1.6 1/ 60
Togian, Sulawesi

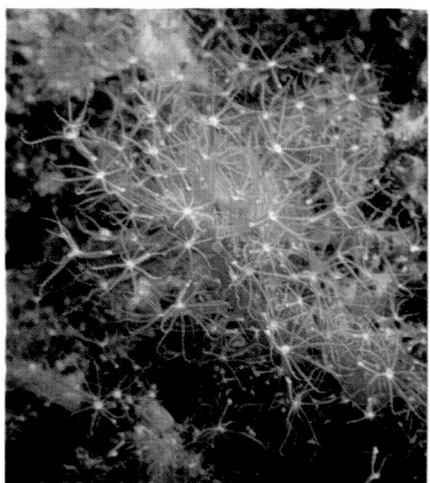

Dendronephythya sp
24mm / f8 1/ 60
Semilan, Thailand

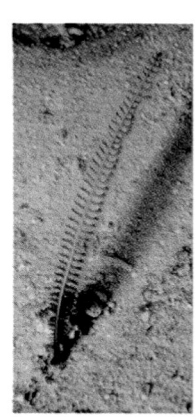

Sea pen
Virgularia sp
60mm / f11 1/ 60
Halmehera, Indonesia

66

Whip coral details
Ctenocella sp.
60mm / f22 , 1/ 60

Delicate sea whip
Junceella fragilis
15mm / f11 , 1/ 60
Nain, Nth Sulawesi

Red whip coral
Ellisella sp.
20mm / f8 , 1/ 60
Susan Reef, Walindi, PNGi

Leather coral / tentacles retracted
Sinularia sp
60mm / f111/ 60
Tioman, Malaysia

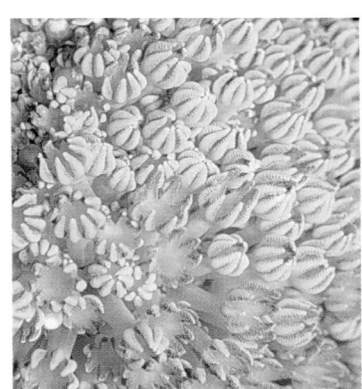 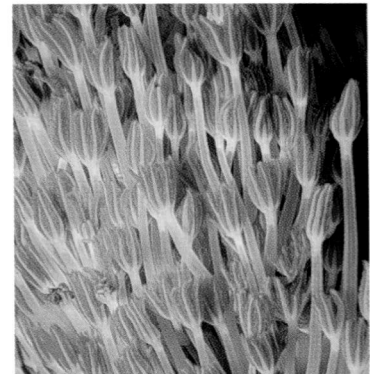

Colour variation of Waving hands soft coral
Xenia *sp.*
60mm / f22 1/ 60

Leather soft coral details
60mm / f22 1/ 60
Bunaken, Nth Sulawesi

Fern tree soft coral
Clavularia sp.
60mm / f22 , 1/ 60
Tukang Besi, Sulawesi

Mushroom soft coral
Sarcophyton sp.
60mm / f11 , 1/ 60
Bunaken, Nth Sulawesi

Nepthea sp.
60mm / f16, 1/ 60
Alor, Indonesiai

Mushroom Soft coral
Sarcophyton sp.
60mm / f22 , 1/ 60
Temple of Doom, Australia GBR

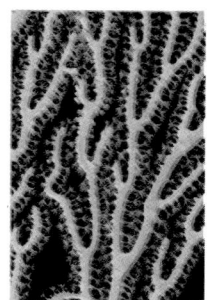

Gorgonian fan details
Semperina & Acabaria sp.
105mm / f22 1/ 125

Semperina gorgonian fanL
60mm / f11 1/ 60
Bunaken, Nth Sulawesi

Gorgeous gorgonian fan
Subergorgia suberosa
20mm / f11 , 1/ 125
PNG

Gorgonia colony with tentacles extended and retracted
Siphonogorgia godeffroyi
20mm / f5.6 , 1/ 60
Walindi, PNG

Sea fan
Melithaea sp.
20mm / f8 , 1/ 60
Tukang Besi, Sulawesi

Gorgonian forest
Subergorgia mollis
20mm / f8 , 1/ 60
Layang Layang, Malaysia

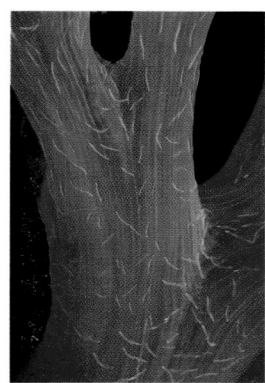

Close-up view of calcareous
particles (sclerites)
Dendronephthya sp.
60mm / f22 , 1/ 60

Dainty soft coral
Chironephthya sp..
60mm / f22, 1/ 60
Kakabia, Indonesia

Dendronephthya sp.
15mm / f5.6 , 1/ 60
Bunaken, Nth Sulawesi

Massive soft coral
Dendronephthya s
15mm / f5.6 , 1/ 6
Holm Reef,
Coral Sea, Australi

72

Umbellate tree coral
Dendronephthya sp.
60mm / f16, 1/ 60
Pulisang, Nth Sulawesi

Soft coral covered reef
Dendronephthya sp.
20mm / f8 , 1/ 60
Maldives

Soft coral colony *Dendronephthya sp.*
20mm / f5.6 , 1/ 60 Walindi, PNG

BLUE & BLACK CORALS

Taxonomically, Black coral in the *Order Antipatharia* is actually more closely related to hard coral, but its whip-like and tree-like growths bear a close resemblance to whip and fan coral. Black corals are not black when alive. Their common name is derived from the colour of their internal skeleton, which is harvested to make into jewelry for the morbid and not so level headed - imagine wearing the skeletons of dead primative animals ! Living black coral comes in luscious brown, shades of yellow and white.

Blue corals (*Heliopora*) resemble hard corals, because of their brittle and massive form, but are in fact more closely related to soft corals. Microscopic examination of the polyps reveal their tentacles to be that of true octocoral.

SOFT CORAL PORTFOLIO

Soft coral pictures brighten an underwater photographer's portfolio and they regularly win at photographic competitions. To capture an image of the foliage of vivid red, pink, orange, green or yellow coloured, flowery soft corals, use your widest angle lens (14mm) together with two powerful strobes set at half power. Shoot against the sky for the magnificent blue water background. To show the internal structure of *Dendronephthya* species, power down your front lighting and position a second strobe from the top.

Spiral wire coral
Cirripathes *sp.*
60mm / f22 , 1/ 60

Black wire coral
Stichopathes sp.
60mm / f22 , 1/ 60

Black coral tree
Antipathes sp.
20mm / f8 , 1/ 60
Sangie , Nth Sulawesi

Black coral tree
Antipathes sp.
20mm / f8 , 1/ 60
Alor, Indonesia

WORMS

PHYLUM PLATYHELMINTHES/ANNELIDA/NEMERTEA/ HEMICHORDATA

The average underwater observer usually doesn't give a marine worm more than a cursory glance. Apart from the fact that worms are inconspicuous, most human association with these wiggly beings rarely goes beyond putting them on the end of the occasional fishing line. From an ecological point of view, marine worms deserve a little more respect. Worms of the sea are like working earth worms in a paddock - cows just chew on grass and contribute to the greenhouse problem by producing vast amounts of methane, while worms maintain and fertilise the habitat by breaking down and recycling the dead plants and organic material. Their tunnels allow air to permeate the ground keeping a whole population of organisms alive. Worms are indeed the quiet achievers.

There are seven phyla of marine worms comprised of over 20,000 different species. However, only four of the more conspicuous groups are focused on in this chapter. They live in a wide range of habitats. Some burrow into living or dead corals, some hide beneath crevices, while others dwell more prominently on other reef invertebrates such as sea cucumbers and sea stars. They can be found everywhere, from the basement of the reef to its abyssal walls. Though more than half the species are worm-shaped, other species vary immensely. Some resemble jellyfish, Christmas trees, and feather dusters while others are flat and colourful more like the nudibranch of the *Mollusc Phylum*.

FLATWORMS PLATYHELMINTHES

Flatworms are rarely recognised for who they really are. Despite being one of the most beautiful of their clan, they are usually mistaken by divers as being just another nudibranch. They have a flattened ovular body, some with prominent, dazzlingly colourful patterns, and they literally glide over the reef.

Flatworms are usually less than 8cm and are simplistic animals with a flattened head, simple organs and eye spots visible only under a microscope. The gliding motion is performed by minute bristles (cilia) on the underside and by muscle contractions over a self-secreted mat of mucus. For a quick leap to "greener pastures", flatworms can take off into the water column by undulating their body margins, their movement as graceful and mesmerising as that of a ballet dancer.

The one tell-tale sign distinguishing flatworms from nudibranchs is that they do not display external gills, nor do they have an anus or a circulatory system. Respiration is by means of diffusing oxygen into the body from the water and the reverse process is used to pass out carbon dioxide. Food is also distributed to the entire body by diffusion.

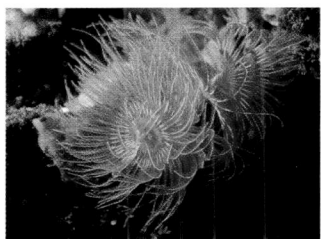

Tube worm
Protula magnifica
*105*mm / f22 , 1/ 60
Bunaken, Indonesia

Elegant tube worm
Filograna elatensis
biggest colony observed
over 1 metre in height
60mm / f16 , 1/ 60
Ruang , Nth Sulawesi

Flat worm
Pseudoceros ferrugineus
105mm / f22 , 1/ 60
Bunaken , Nth Sulawesi

The most important concern of flatworms is the survival of their species and they possess both complex male and female reproductive organs ie, they are hermaphrodites. However, procreation must still be performed by two separate individuals in an "I'll pass you some of my sperm, if you pass me some of your eggs" pact. Fertilised eggs are laid out on the substrata in a twirl, similar to an open-ended circle. The egg ribbon spirals of some flat worms resemble those of the nudibranch. To save time, busy flatworms can also regenerate a whole new animal from a detached fragment.

Flatworms are carnivores, feeding on detritus and ascidians of the reef, but they themselves make a lousy item on the aquatic menu. As with all brightly coloured marine animals, their bodies are toxic and distasteful. I once saw a Titan Triggerfish swallow one of these "candies" of the blue the fish spat out the victim almost instantaneously.

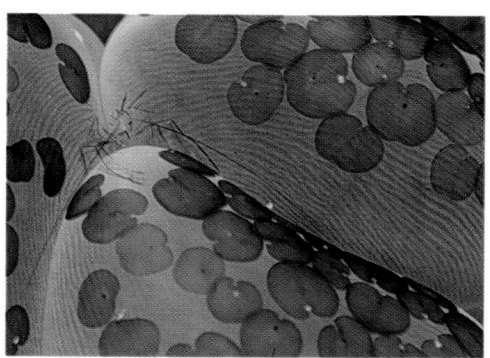

Flatworms on bubble coral with commensal shrimp.
Waminoa sp. with Vir philippinensis
105mm / f22, 1/ 60
Bunaken, Nth Sulawesi

SEGMENTED WORMS ANNELIDA / POLYCHAETES

With more than 12,000 species and 70 families worldwide, segmented worms are one of the major players in the animal kingdom. They have a metamerically segmented body of bilateral symmetry meaning that their bodies are in similarly segmented sections. They bear sophisticated organs for different functions, including a complete digestive system, but they have a closed circulatory system. Ecologically, there are two types of annelids those that are free living or sedentary burrowing, and those that are tube dwelling suspension or detritus feeders.

Christmas tree segmented worm.
Spirobranchus giganteus
105mm / f22, 1/ 125
Komodo, Indonesia

Note the tube
is completely
burrowed in coral.
Protula magifica
60mm / f22, 1/ 60
Tioman, Malaysia

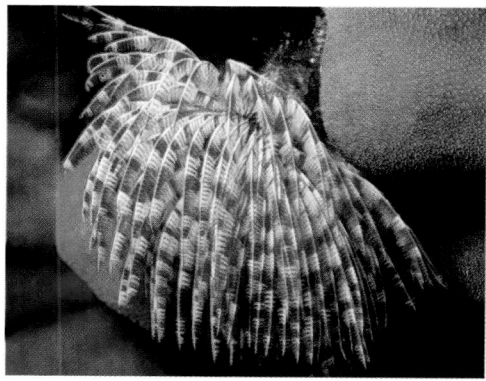

Tube worm.
Sabellastarte indica
60mm / f22, 1/ 60
Pulisang, Nth Sulawesi

MOBILE WORMS

Free living worms are in the subclass of *Errantia* and live beneath rocks, in coral crevices in abandoned shells or burrowed deep into mud and sand flats. They are mainly active at night and their bodies are lined with setae (bristles) for protection. These worms resemble the terrestrial centipedes. Their bodies have numerous segments, with similar head and tail sections. They are active predators the creepy crawlies of the reef. Fire worms belong to the *Amphinomidae* family and have needle-like setae which may also contain venom and can inflict great pain when handled.

The sex life of annelids is as diverse as their life styles and varies from simply releasing eggs and sperm into the water column, to more unusual variations. Free living polycheates are separately sexed and produce eggs and sperm inside their body cavity. In one of nature's oversights, however aroused they are, these worms have no suitable opening in their body to release their sperm and eggs. Instead these worm choose to die for the survival of their species. On a certain night of the year, sexually mature males and females gather in masses and ascend toward the surface for one incredible orgy. As they reach the apex, their movement becomes erratic and the pushing, pounding and violent muscular contractions literally tear or blow their bodies apart so that their sperm and eggs may meet to produce a new generation. This is the ultimate sacrifice.

The Palolo worms (*genus Eunice*) have their own variation of such a sacrifice. Sexually mature adults are able to accumulate their eggs or sperm to their tail segment. In the South Pacific, one week after the November full moon, their tails become detached to float to the surface. So it is tails of eggs and sperm making whoopi on the surface breaking apart to develop into swimming larvae.

UNWORM-LIKE WORMS

Sedentary worms include Christmas trees (*Serpulidae*), feather dusters (*Sabellidae*) and tube worms, which make tubes out of calcium carbonate secreted from their own bodies. Living in these self-built apartments, they are completely sheltered from waves predators and currents. These animals are light-sensitive, the slightest movement or passing shadow will cause them to contract. Sedentary worms cannot move around and thus are filter feeders, trapping organic debris in moving water with their specialised fine nets. Tube worms of the family *Terebellidae* have tentacles with tiny grooves on their undersides which are lined with microscopic cilia and coated with sticky mucus. After dark, the worms send out their tentacles to sweep the reef bed for edible items. The microscopic cilia move the food particles back to the mouth like sending food on a conveyor belt.

Sexes are also separate among sedentary polychaete worms. At nature's cue, eggs and sperm are released simultaneously into the sea. Fertilised eggs develop into larvae and normally stay in the planktonic layer for 23 weeks. Once happy with their free spirit days, young worms settle on a coral head, or any other suitable surface, secreting a tube to kill the underlying polyps. New coral grows quickly to surround the tube. Meanwhile, the new occupant defies eviction by secreting additional tube material to keep pace with the coral.

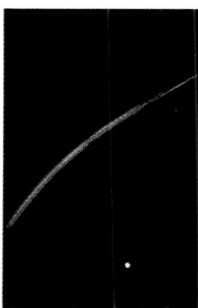

SPAWNING SEQUENCE
OF THE
ANNELID WORM

The worms attempt to tear themselves apart by stretching up to 10 times their body size.

When they contract like a rubberband, they fall to the ground and break apart.

Bang..the explosion, sperm and eggs are released into the water. The worm dies.

Pherecardia sp.
105mm, f16 , 1/ 125
Biaro, Nth Sulawesi (1994)

RIBBON WORMS PHYLUM NEMERTEA

Most of the 900 known species of ribbon worms are marine dwellers and are commonly found on coral reefs, beneath rocks or buried in sand. As their name suggests, they are soft bodied, flattened, elongated and unsegmented. Their diet is comprised of tiny invertebrates and their own eggs! In some ways they are similar to the turbellarians. They have external cilia, secrete mucus on their trail and their nervous systems are nearly identical. Most species are 2-3 cm in length but a few odd individuals have been found to reach over 2m. The most notable feature of ribbon worms is their possession of a hollow, muscular proboscis, which is armed with a piercing stylet used to capture prey.

ACORN WORMS

We chose to discuss this inconspicuous, seldom seen worm of the *Phylum Hemichorta* simply because most divers will at one time or another observe a very distinctive and unusual feces a coil like patch on the sandy reef. They are sand deposits created by acorn worms above their burrow, perhaps to foil potential predators. They certainly fool divers into not ambling too close.

Marine worms are one of the world's great animal groups and occur in vast numbers. They play a significant ecological role in the chain of life in any marine habitat. From the free living worms to the dazzling sedentary Christmas tree worms, they are among some of the least understood and least appreciated invertebrates on the reef.

WORM PICTURES

Worms are small, so a 105mm macro lens plus lots of film and patience is essential for that award-winning worm picture. Christmas trees and feather duster worms look great against a black background. Look for one that sits high on the crest of a massive coral, and shoot against a water background. If you have been waiting for a pig to fly, a flatworm will take-off in front of your eyes. Grab that shot, they make a great picture.

Elegant tube worm
Filograna elatensis
60mm / f16 , 1/ 60
Halmehera , Indonesia

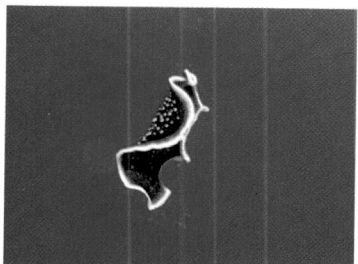

Thysanozoon nigropapillosum
105mm / f5.6 , 1/ 250
Sipadan, Malaysia
* note the change in background
colour with change of exposure
settings and strobe power.

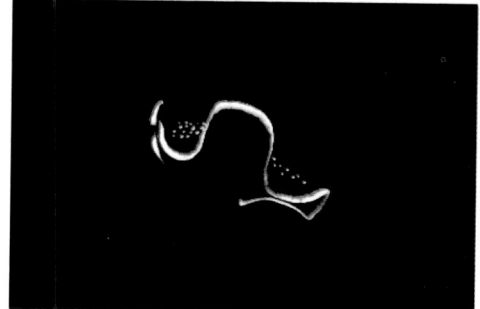

A flatworm might literally
'take off' to greener pasture!
Thysanozoon nigropapillosum
105mm / f22 , 1/ 125
Sipadan, Malaysia

Terebellied worm
sweeping the reef
floor for food.
Terebellied polychaete
60mm / f16 , 1/ 60
Temple of Doom,
GBR, Australia

SEA SHELLS - PHYLUM MOLLUSCA

Not long ago, in Sudan, you could actually trot down the Nile Valley and buy a wife with shells. You would, of course, need a wallet the size of a jumbo plane - a young wife cost 100,000 cowries, though older women generally were marked down to 20,000. Besides using sea shells to trade for wives, and to feast on, our ancestors found an endless use for shells - as jewellry, musical instruments, teapots, spoons, lamps, dyes, decor, wash basins, floor tiles, money and buttons. The most creative use came from the Italian who harvested the Pen shells (genus *Pinna*) for golden threads to manufacture fine robes, gloves and capes. Unfortunately, the supply of shells was not infinite and many shells are now either extinct or have become incredibly rare due to human greed and abuse.

Sea shells belong to the *Phylum Mollusca*, which is comprised of at least 112,000 species and categorised into four classes: *Gastropoda*, *Bivalvia*, *Polyplacophora* and *Cephalopoda*. Different types of molluscs exhibit amazing diversity - from microscopic shell gastropoda and vivid coloured nudibranchs, to chambered nautilus and 20m long giant squids. In brief, molluscs are soft-bodied animals with no bones. Most have hard external shells, others have internal shells, but one thing that all molluscs have in common is a foot which is used for different purposes in each class. Species from each class are easily distinguishable by their body plan with gills for breathing, a simple head with sensory cells, mouth, sex and excretory organs.

GASTROPODA (UNIVALVES)

The dominent class of the clan, with over 90,000 species in several families worldwide, *Gastropoda* are sought after indiscriminately for their shells. Gastropods, or snails, belong the subclass of *Prosobranchia*. Snail-like, with coiled or cone shells, they include cowries, helmets, tritons, murex, winkles and top shells. Some gastropods, through the millenniums, have discarded their shells and are classified as *Opisthobranchia* (see "Nudibranchs", p92). In spite of their abundance, gastropods are often inconspicuous on coral reefs, hidden under coral crevices, rubble and sandy beds. The hard protective cone or coiled shell on their backs is the refuge into which they retreat to escape from potential predators. The shell is secreted by the mantle, a fleshy tissue-like skin, and has three or more layers. The inner layer is made of calcium carbonate crystals, carefully positioned in various configurations in a protein matrix. The mantle adds to the inner layers throughout the snail's life, thus the shell gets thicker as the animal grows.

The other body part usually exposed is the muscular foot, which is often extended to provide slow but sturdy locomotion. For ease of motion the foot secretes a kind of a foot lubricant to cut down friction on the rubbery sole. When disturbed, the foot is completely retracted, and in some species the shell has a kind of membranous sheath (operculum) which shuts the opening like a "heavy metal trap door". The mantle of some species of cowries and their cousins can often be observed enveloping the outer surface of the

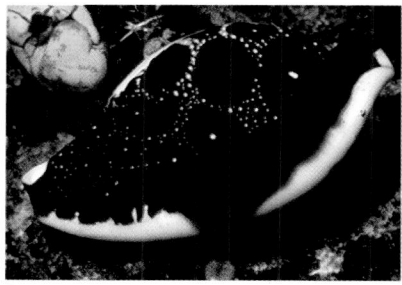

Egg cowrie
Ovula ovum.
60mm f11 , 1/ 60
Pulau Pombo,Maluku

Nassarius papillosus
60mm / f22 , 1/ 60
Kahahetang, Nth Sulawesi

Bat Volute
Cymbiola verspertilo
60mm / f22 , 1/ 60
Kelasey, Nth Sulawesi

Allied egg cowrie
on soft coral
seudosimnia marginata
105mm / f22 , 1/ 60
Coral Sea, Australia

WHAT,S FOR DINNER?

The diets of Gastropods are as varied as their kind, ranging from algae and echinoderms (sea stars, sea urchins) to tiny crustaceans and fishes. Feeding is performed by their retractable proboscis or trunk which contains a tongue-shaped radula - a flexible skin lined with hundreds of tiny teeth. Some conus species have feeding radulas that make the M16 rifle pale in comparison. Cone shells hunt by extending their modified proboscis. When prey is within range, the proboscis launches a harpoon-like tooth that pierces the prey (fish or worm) and injects a deadly venom. The proboscis is then retracted, hauling the prey in. The venom is deadly and even a small dosage is powerful enough to cause fatality to unwary humans who may put these cones in their pockets. Marine photographers have recently observed some sea snails behaving like "vampires of the sea". These animals are capable of extending the proboscis deep into the gills or mouth of a sleeping parrotfish and literally suck blood as if through a straw in a bottle.

Gastropods can be separate sex or hermaphroditic, but cross-sexual reproduction is a must. Sea snails are solitary with no social organisation, hence interaction between individuals occurs purely for the sake of sex. Mating is normally in pairs, with the male positioned next to the female's body, transferring and receiving sperm to fertilise eggs which are laid out in a spiraled mass which may contain up to one million eggs. Snails make lousy parents. The fertilised eggs remain bonded together and are left on their own in a thick mucus layer until they hatch. Most species spend some time in the planktonic zone before settling down to live their life on the reef

Spawning - the female lays the eggs,
the male fertilises with sperms.
Cypraea sp.
60mm / f16, 1/ 60
Kahahetang, Nth Sulawesi

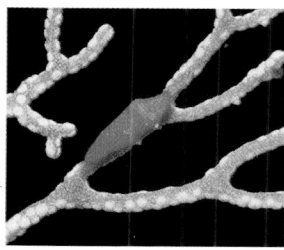

Allied cowrie
on gorgonian fan.
Primoulee sp.
105mm / f22 , 1/ 60
Limbe Strait, Nth Sulawesi

Tiger cowrie
Cypraea tigris
60mm / f16 , 1/ 60
Kelasey, Nth Sulawesi

Turban shell feeding
on Halamedia
Turbo petholatus
60mm / f16 , 1/ 60
GBR, Australia

Helmet shell
Casmaria ponderosa
60mm / f22 , 1/ 60
Kelasey, Nth Sulawesi

BIVALVIA (BIVALVES) - MOLLUSCS WITH TWO SHELLS

Bivalves are the shells most common to us, the shells we eat, the shells that monitor the quality of our waterway, the shell on top of petrol stations all over the world. There are about 15,000 described species of two-shell molluscs including oysters, clams, scallops and mussels. Bivalves are easily recognisable, always having two shells of hinged at the dorsal margin. The animal lives laterally compressed inside, and can open and close the shell valves by contracting or relaxing a single large muscle, the adductor muscle which is attached to the inside of the valves. The mantle of scallops and some oysters bears numerous iridescent, primitive, sparkling eyes, sensitive to changes in light intensity, along a fold on its lips called the velar fold. The mantle lobes are often fused and may extend as one of two openings or siphons through which water is pumped in and out to provide respiration. As such, bivalves are filter feeders, ingesting nutritious plankton and micro-organisms which are pumped in and out through the siphons. Famous molluscs like the *Tridacna gigas* (Giant clams), which dwell in shallow water supplement their food supply by harbouring the algae cells, zooxanthellae. The zooxanthellae produce nutrients for their host through the process of photosynthesis but the host may also harvest some of the zooxanthellae to eat. Giant clams do not eat human beings. Stories of them gobbling up divers are purely seafarers yarns after one beer too many.

Though bivalves are endowed with a foot, they do not move around very often. Most attach to or burrowed into the substratum, either permanently, like oysters, or temporarily, like mussels. Some are free living. Scallops can swim by rapidly opening and closing their shell and they also use this technique to squirt water at impending threats or to frighten off predators. The Flame File shell is a remarkable species undertaking long swims across reef beds by clapping its two valves together and expelling propulsive jets of water from spaces alongside the auricles or "ears" of its shell. Such movement makes the animal looks like a pair of sensuous flaming lips running about on the reef - these lips are definitely foul to kiss.

Bivalves are described as sequential hermaphrodites, meaning that they have both male and female organs but, during mating time, they either eject sperm first, and egg a few hours later, or vice versa. Like corals, to maximise the production of little bivalves spawning in a local area is perfectly synchronised, possibly by water temperature or nature's own biological "Rolex" timepiece. One of the most incredible wildlife experiences is to be caught within a mass spawning of Giant clams. It is like swimming into an upsidedown snow storm among erupting geysers and volcanoes. Fertilised eggs hatch out as veliger larvae, to drift in the open sea for between two and 40 days before settling down to begin life on the reef.

Thorny oyster
Spondylus sp.
60mm / f22 , 1/ 60
Alor, Indonesia

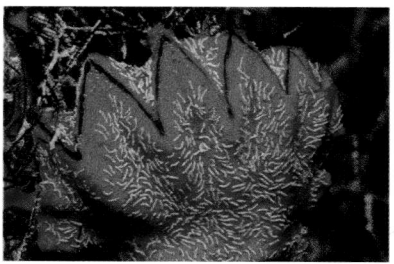

Cocks comb oyster
Lopha cristagalli
60mm / f16 , 1/ 60
Bontang, Indonesia

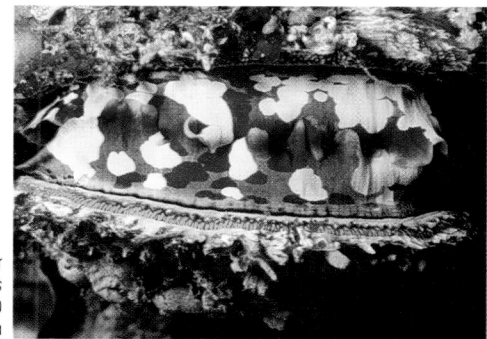

Thorny oyster
Spondylus varians
60mm / f16 , 1/ 60
Layang Layang, Malaysia

Over 1m *Giant Clam*
Tridacna gigas
20mm / f11 , 1/ 60
GBR, Australia

CHITONS - ANCIENT MOLLUSCS (POLYPLACOPHORA)

Chitons are the most primitive molluscs, with worm-like bodies comprised of eight separate overlapping shell plates encircled by a fleshy mantle. When threatened, a chiton can roll itself into a ball, exposing only the hard shell. As ancient animals they are slow moving, using an oval, foot-like appendage, and dwell almost exclusively on shallow subtidal zones and rocky sea shores.

One of the few vegetarian molluscs, Chiton feed by using their wide, many-toothed ribbon-like radula, like a rasping tongue, to scrape minute algae and seaweed off rocks. Male chitons are deprived of a penis, so when the time is right, sperm are simply released into the water. This arouses the females to either emit eggs or allow the sperm to be drawn into their mantle cavities by means of water movement through respiration. Some species are known to brood their young while others lay egg strings which are attached to the substrate.

PICTURES OF MOLLUSCS

The biggest problem with photographing molluscs is that you have to find them first. Most molluscs are inconspicuous on a reef, so knowledge of their habitat is important. One of my favourites are allied cowries which live on gorgonian fans. Take a closer and longer look next time to find these gorgeous cowries that have a mantle identical to the colour of their host. Approach bivalves slowly and carefully. Avoid spooking them or they will shut their mantles before your face. 1:1 macro 60mm and 105mm lenses are essential.

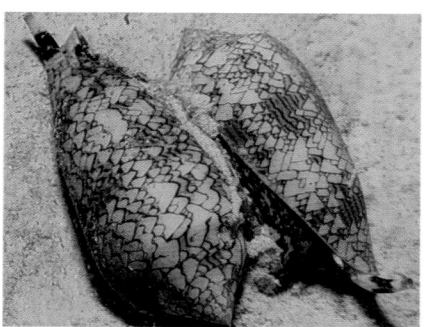

Textile cone shell - this one has killed many human predators, who have tried to collect them.
Conus textile
l60mm / f16 , 1/ 60
Siladen, Nth Sulawesi

Flame file shell
Limaria sp.
60mm / f16 , 1/ 60
Alor, Indonesia

Caught this Flame file shell
out 'swimming ' in the open.
Limaria sp.
60mm / f16 , 1/ 60
Alor, Indonesia

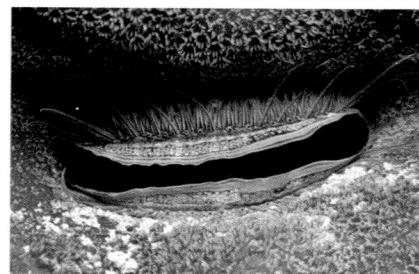

Pedum shell embedded in coral boulder.
. Note the minute eyes along its lips. (mantle)
Pedum spondyloideum
60mm / f16 , 1/ 60
Sipadan, Malaysia

Tridacna crocea
60mm / f11 , 1/ 60
Derawan, East Kalimantan

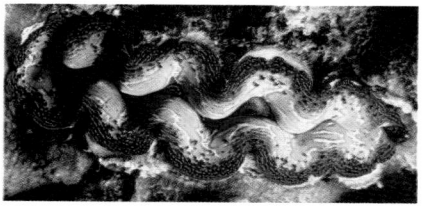

Safely burrowed in coral from predators.
Tridacna bivalve shells
Tridacna derasa, T. squamosa, T. maxima.
24mm / f11 , 1/ 60
Bunaken, Nth Sulawesi

Nudibranchs - Mollusca, Subclass Opisthobranchia

Nudibranchs are the razzle-dazzle punks of coral reefs. They are outrageous, loud, bizarre, trend-setters and have a ruffled elegance. They come in every conceivable colour combination from the Pantone colour guide, but, since they evolved long before the technique of modern process printing, they might be well have been created by company of historic artists such as Matisse, Miro or Picasso. They are strictly aquatic and there are at least 3,000 species in the world oceans, ranging from a few species in the Antarctic, to the warm water of the Indo-Pacific reefs where 2,000 species congregate. Their habitat ranges from intertidal rock pools and the planktonic realm, to over 100m deep abyssal walls. There are no strict rules as to where nudibranchs might be found. They live wherever you find them, usually near the feeding ground unique to each individual species, but they are "here today, gone tomorrow" characters. Nudibranchs and company are close relatives of gastropoda and bivalves. It appears that they became weary of carrying a home on their back and thus discarded the hard shell through evolution. "Nudibranch" really means "naked-gills" and refers to the exposed respiratory organs positioned along their backs, either as a tuft of feather duster-like gills or as a series of finger-like appendages known as cerata, which also serve as part of their digestive and defence system. Most nudibranchs are small creatures ranging from minute to just a few centimetres, but their related bigger cousins of the families *Pleurobranchidae* and *Aplysiidae* can grow up to 50 cm. True nudibranchs in the order of *Nudibranchia* are divided into four main types.

- The Harlequin Nudibranchs, doridaceans or dorids, are the dominating group and are characterised by the presence of two horn-like tentacles, or rhinopores, on the head and the feathery gills on the back, which are retractable when threatened.

- The second largest group are the Tubercular Nudibranchs, aeolidaceans or aeolids, they are easily recognisable by their finger-like cerata appendages which are non retractable.

- The Side-gilled Nudibranchs, dendrotaceans, are like the aeolids, with side gills but have a cup-liked sheath around their rhinopores which are retractable.

- The Veiled Nudibranchs, arminaceans, are distinguishable by an enlarged fleshy lobe on the head and longitudinal ridges on the back.

Broad-minded Sex

Being one of the most pretty animals, and of hermaphrodite background, individual function as both male and female. However, they are always male when they mate and self-fertilisation is not practised probably because they wouldn't forgive themselves in the morning. When two mating males find each other, they lie alongside with their right sides almost touching, so that their genital aperture can be extended to make connection. This intimate bonding may last from a few minutes to a number of hours. After sufficient sperm packages have been exchanged, the couple goes their separate ways and each dons the female role to lay out pretty lace or ribbon strings of eggs. These may contain up to one million eggs in some species. All species spawn once then die- it is no wonder that there are no old wrinkly nudibranchs. In some species, eggs are laid out near their food source, for example, near sponges or algae. Upon hatching little replicas of the adult simply start to feed. Other species hatch into veliger larvae which drift in oceanic currents for a period varying from a few days to several months

Awesome harlequin nudibranch
Notodoris minor
60mm / f22 , 1/ 125
Limbe Strait, Nth Sulawesi

Tubercular nudibranch
Phyllodesmium kabiranum
105mm / f16 1/ 60
Sangalaki, East Kalimantan

Solor Powered nudibranch
Phyllodesmium longicirra
105mm / f22, 1/ 60 / Taka Bonarate, Sth Sulawesi

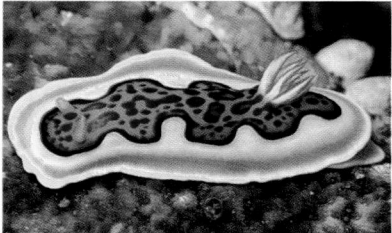

Dorid nudibranch
Chromodoris gleniei
105mm / f16, 1/ 60
Maldives

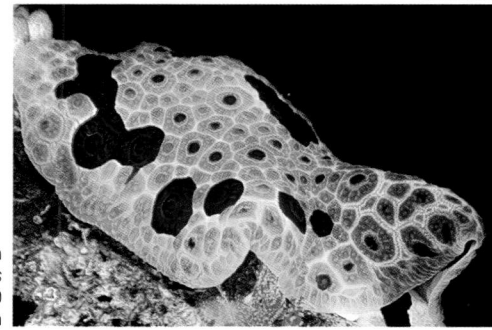

Pleurobranch
Pleurobranchus grandis
60mm / f16 , 1/ 60
Derawan, East Kalimantan

Senses and Sensibilities

Nudibranchs are often observed feeling their way across the reef bed with their rhinopores. The rhinopores are sensitive to light and chemicals, enabling them to locate food and potential mates. Nudibranchs may be seen browsing on sessile animals such as sponges or bryozoans. Most species have specific diets and are always found near their food source. A few species of nudibranch (*Phyllodesmium longicirra, Glaucidae*), never have to worry about shopping for dinner. In fact, they hardly need to eat at all. More or less solar-powered, they have their own energy manufacturing plant of zooxanthellae algae on their cerata. These microscopic plants produce carbohydrates through photosynthesis which are absorbed by the host as nutrition. These ingenious animals never have to work for their next meal!

Most nudibranchs are carnivores, with a diet ranging from anemones, hydroids, corals, sponges, fish eggs or tunicates, to various crutaceans. The diet may be varied or specific, depending on the species. Nudibranchs generally use their radula, a file-like mouthpiece with thousands of teeth, to break off chunks of prey. However, a few species are known to punch holes and suck up the inside soft tissues. Some specialised dendronotacean Melibe species have a gossamer hood around their mouth which can stretch enormously to engulf their crustacean prey.

Candies from Hell

Nudibranchs, being as colourful and interestingly shaped as lollies in a candy store, must surely entice other sea creatures to take a nibble or two. As fishes and their associates might tell you, that is not a good idea. Though nudibranchs exhibit colours and patterns that seem to scream, "eat me", these little conniving fellows have some pretty nasty surprises in store for potential predators. Since nudibranchs prey on sponges, hydroids, anemones and bryozoans, all of which have mean defence systems, they have developed the ability to use these nasty, potent and ugly weapons for their own devices. A very neat trick that some aeolid nudibranchs have is the ability to store living cells from their prey, as well as their toxins. When these nudibranchs eat an anemone or hydroid, for example, the stinging cells are captured, preserved and transferred through their digestive tract to the tips of their cerata. The stinging cells are kept alive to defend their adopted host. When harassed, they simply wave their cerata about in a display of warning, and when touched by, say, a fish, the stinging cells are discharged, driving toxins into the predator. How these nudibranchs manage to prevent the stinging cells from firing into their own body is one of many biological mysteries. This form of protection is so effective that even big fish are well taught, knowing to leave these little nasties of the reef alone. Other nudibranchs are very well camouflaged. Colouration and body designs make them blend in with the environment so that they can be very difficult for predators to locate.

Nudies Pictures

I always have time for nudibranchs. They don't move too quickly and their vivid colouration makes great pictures. A 105mm lens is necessary and try shooting them at eye level to show their muscular foot and waving gills against a blue or black background.

Reticulidia halgerda
60mm / f22 , 1/ 60
Halmehera , Indonesia

Glossodoris electra.
60mm / f22 , 1/ 125
Alor, Indonesia

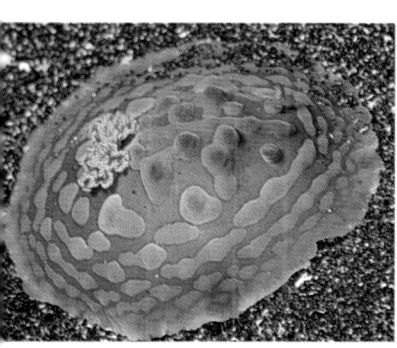

Asteronotus cespitosus
60mm / f22 , 1/ 125
Kelasey, Nth Sulawesi

Unnamed specie
60mm / f22 , 1/ 125
Ambon, Indonesia

Egg masses are usually laid out
in an anti-clockwise direction.
105mm / f22 , 1/ 60

'Link up' to mate
Nembrotha sp.
60mm / f16 , 1/ 60
Byron Bay, Australia

CEPHALOPODS PHYLUM MOLLUSCA

"The tiger can only devour you - the octopus inhales you; to be eaten alive is terrible, to be drunk alive is inexpressible" Victor Hugo

The reputation of cephalopods is not just fiction material from Jules Verne's epic science fiction tale "Twenty Thousand Leagues Under the Sea". A recent nightmarish encounter with giant Humboldt squids (*Dosidicus gigas*) by marine photographer Alex Kerstitch was not Hollywood sensationalism, but a real life experience. He was struck by three 9ft (3m) squids three times in one night, wrapped by supple, but "tough as steel", tentacles round his chest, neck, head and waist. In desperation he bit into the Humboldt but the animal still had a good grip on his dive computer. It swam off into the darkness, still gripping the computer which was attached to Alex's regulator. He was hurled along like a puppy on a leash. Fortunately, the console tore off, but the thieving squid escaped with the computer, as well as a thick gold chain and dive light. Alex fortunately also escaped to tell his story.

Adventurers of the sea are fortunate that most cephalopods are not aggressive, though they are highly intelligent animals with advanced sensory organs and responsive nervous systems. Their eyes are human-like, capable of registering shapes, textures and colours. Endowed with a well-developed brain, they are the most sophisticated of all invertebrates, demonstrating complex and intriguing behaviours superior to that of both fishes and amphibians. There are over 750 species of cephalopods, comprised of octopus, squid, cuttlefish and nautilus, inhabiting every conceivable habitat in the ocean. Cephalopod literally means "head-foot", from the Greek *kephal* ("head") and *podas* ("foot"), referring aptly to the animal's tentacles, or "arms and legs", which are attached to its head.

In simplistic terms, cephalopods are soft-bodied molluscs. Without an internal skeleton, and having limbs without joints, cephalopods have a form of modified shell which is mostly hidden inside their soft tissues for some secondary function.

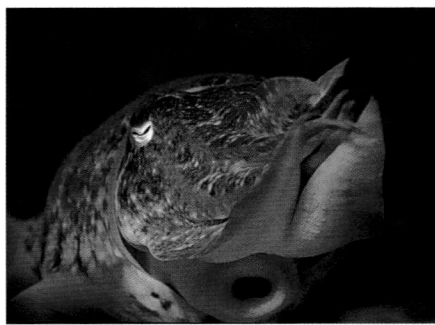

Tropical cuttlefish
Sepia latimanus
60mm / f11 , 1/ 60
Nain, Nth Sulawesi

Reef octopus
Octopus cyanea
60mm / f16 , 1/ 60
Temple of Doom, GBR, Australia

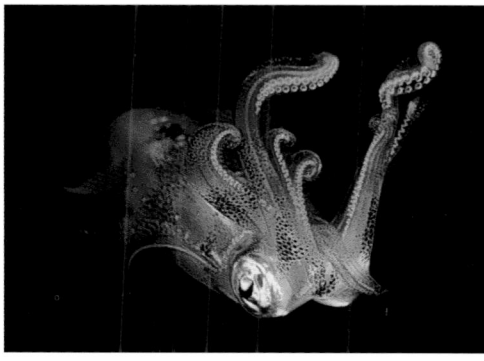

Tropical squid (found near surface to 100m)
Sepioteuthis lessoniana
60mm / f16 , 1/ 60
Kelasey, Nth Sulawesi

Tropical cuttlefish
Sepia latimanus
28mm / f11 , 1/ 60
Bunaken, Nth Sulawesi

CEPHALOPODS IN BRIEF

Octopus - have eight arms (tentacles) and are mostly bottom feeders. They do not possess fins or an internal shell and normally move by crawling but will use jet propulsion to escape from predators. They practise a relationship which is one of the few within the animal kingdom , humans included, that can be said to be truly monogamous. Male and females do not mate with any other partners besides the chosen one. Shortly after the female has her offspring, she dies, but the male stays on. He does not ever mate again.

Cuttlefish - have eight short arms lined with suckers, and two longer specialised arms (lacking in octopus), with suckers only on the tips. Their swimming motion is similar to skate or ray. They undulate their lateral fins for stability, steering and slow swimming. Cuttlefish have a large flat internal shell or cuttlebone which appears to be used for regulating buoyancy as they hover near the bottom.

Squid - like cuttlefish, they have ten arms. Squid are really a streamlined, faster version of cuttlefish, with cuttlebone replaced by a lightweight horny structure which acts as a support for muscles and other tissues. They tend to hunt for fast moving fish such as mackerel but may also attack bottom dwelling crustaceans. Orange-sized sucker scars from squids have been found on pelagic sharks.

Chambered Nautilus - is the most primitive and archaic cephalopod, with ancestry dating back some 400 million years to a time when it was the highest life form in the sea. With only four species in their class, they are living fossils. Their suckerless arms and eyes without lenses gives the nautilus a close resemblance to ammonites, creatures that dominated the ocean before the dinosaur. The nautilus is the only cephalopod with a true shell, made of many chambers, which not only protects the animal but serves to regulate buoyancy. The nautilus inhabits the deep abyssal depths of the sea by day but undertakes nightly vertical migrations of several hundred metres toward the surface to search for food.

JET PROPULSION & SMOKE SCREENS

Jet propulsion is ancient technology for cephalopods. A quick getaway is achieved by the cephalopod by drawing water through its mantle cavity, then contracting a series of muscles to forcibly expel the water out of its siphon. The siphon is like a jet exhaust. Depending on which direction it is pointing, the animal can attain rapid swimming speed either forward or backward.

Squid, cuttlefish and the octopus also have another secret weapon up their tubular sleeve, namely, a large sac containing a fluid with black sepio-melanin pigment - the same substance that turns our skin dark. When they are alarmed or threatened, the ink is ejected to create a smoke screen in one direction while the animal hightails it off in the other. This ink is suspected to contain irritating anaesthetic substances to fend off predators.

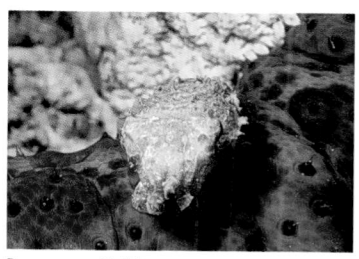

Papuan cuttlefish
Sepia papuensis
60mm / f22 , 1/ 60
Hatta Island, Maluku, Indonesia

Tropical cuttlefish - note the colour it has assumed
over the soft coral.
Sepia latimanus
20mm / f8 , 1/ 60, Derawan, East Kalimantani

Red octopus
Octopus luteus
60mm / f11 , 1/ 60
Pulisang, Nth Sulawesi

Bob tail squid - this specie is capable of burying
themselves completely beneath sand
to escape predation
Eupyrmna sp.
105mm / f22 , 1/ 125   Kelasey, Nth Sulawesi

Bob tail squid
Eupyrmna sp.
105mm / f22 , 1/ 125
Derawan, East Kalimantan

EYE TO EYE

With regard to the ratio of body to eye, the squid wins hands down over all animals humans included. This is not only true for the biggest invertebrate in the world, the giant squid (*Architeuthis dux* - the biggest recorded specimen of which measures 20m) but for most specimens. Their binocular vision is near human standard. With excellent depth and ground perception, they are capable of interpreting patterns, density and colour variations of moving objects, permitting recognition of complex forms - no matter which way a squid rotates, their eyes work like the bubble in a spirit level, adjusting to see perspective the right side up.

A LANGUAGE OF COLOUR AND PATTERNS

Squid and their kin can change colour in less than 2/3 of a second to camouflage themselves, to reflect emotions such as alarm or aggression and to send sexual signals. Colour change is achieved by three layers of cell structures, called chromatophores which are filled with colour pigment bright yellow near the surface, and an orange layer above a dark base enabling a play of colour. The chromatophores are like miniature plastic bags which are expanded by radial muscles under a dual nervous system controlled locally and centrally. When contracted, a pattern of fine striping is seen while expansion spreads out all layers of chromatophores, colouring the squid like a rainbow. Embedded above and below the chromatophores are another type of cell containing laminar crystals called iridocytes. These are like microscopic reflectors. When light falls on them through the chromatophores, there is a play of light and colours enhancing the chromatophores. As the cells expand and contract, a technicoloured light show can be seen from the head across the body. This light show is the perfect example of the most powerful neurological system known to man, making the animal's colour change and camouflage abilities unrivaled in the animal kingdom.

Squid language is a visual reality with a repertoire of at least 16 different patterns recorded - from stripes, splotches, rings, spots, lateral flames and lateral blushing to downright "naughty'" accentuated testes. Changes of patterns are used for communication among their own kind.

SNAP A SNACK

Cephalopods are pretty cool when it comes to snatching quick snacks off the reef. Cuttlefish and squid often go stalking for little fishes or crustaceans with their two longer prehensile tentacles uncoiled. Once close enough, the tentacles lash out like a whip as fast as 1/3 of a second, to grab their prey. Retrieving inward, the other arms hold the food in place for the animal's very powerful parrot-like beak. The upper mandible closes within the lower, so that the sharp edges of each cut obliquely, like a pair of scissors. The animal bites off the entire fish head first, followed by little chunks, until the guts and tail are discarded. An octopus is better adapted to hunting close to the bottom. It will often crawl across the sea floor feeling in holes and crevices with tentacle tips for crabs or lobsters. Once contact is made, the octopus holds onto its victim with suckers and pulls them out, to their mouth.

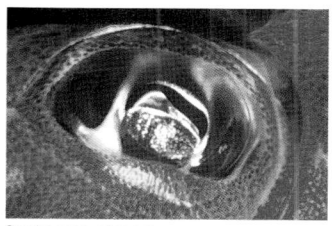

Squid eye, almost
identical to humans.
Sepia sp.
105mm / f22 , 1/ 125
PNG

Extremely flexible, octopus can
squeeze into small crevices.
Undescribed sp.
60mm / f11 , 1/ 60
Ruang, Nth Sulawesi

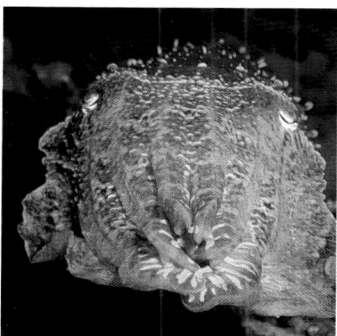

Cuttlefish language - note the accentuated
notches, pattern and colours, all of which are
visual signals.
Sepia latimanus
28mm / f11 , 1/ 60 Bunaken, Nth Sulawesi

Using her two specialised tentacles,
eggs are deposited deep into
fire coral to avoid predation.
Sepia latimanus
60mm / f11 , 1/ 60 Nain, Nth Sulawesi

Cuttlefish maternal duties.
Over 6 hours, this female
lay over 100 eggs.
Sepia latimanus
60mm / f11 , 1/ 60 Nain, Nth Sulawesi

TENDER LOVING CUDDLES

Considering the sophisticated behaviour of cephalopods, it would not be hard to imagine cephalopods engaging in cuddles and whip-snapping sexual routines especially when they are endowed with eight to ten sucking arms. Another impressive thing about these male cuddlers is that they package their sperm into tiny convenient packets called spermatophores - stored away prepared for the "Saturday night out".

To attract a female into his arms, the male cephalopod goes through a cephalopod mating "song and dance" routine with his tentacles, showing off his best "lightshow" and eventually turning vividly red before copulation. The pair mate, reaching out and interlocking with all their ten "arms and legs", at which point the male reaches into his "coat pocket" with his modified arm, called a hectocotylus, and pulls out a packet of sperm which he deposits deep into the female's mantle cavity.

In some cases fertilisation is not immediate, but usually the sperm packet "explodes" and the sperm whizzes off on its way to the female ovaries. The female proceeds to lay the eggs, fertilise them and attach them amongst fire corals, moorings or any other fixed structure with lots of water movement for aeration. This maternal chore may last from six hours to a number of days. Many species hang around until their young have emerged and many never survive to breed a second time, dying from exhaustion and stress in the process.

Squid lay elongated white cases filled with clusters of eggs, while cuttlefish produce ping-pong ball-shaped eggs. An octopus deposits clusters and strands of eggs in rocky crevices and the clutch is guarded until hatching. Incubation lasts from 10 days to three weeks and often, just before hatching, the little eyes of the developing young can be seen in their translucent capsules. When hatched they are immediate replicas of the adults, capable of squirting ink when threatened and of changing colours and patterns.

PORTFOLIO OF CEPHALOPODS

I love cephalopods, there are never enough of them in my portfolio. They are animals capable of learning from experience, thus, with some gentle encouragement, you can photograph them like old "Fido" in the backyard. From a macro shot of a squid's eye to a fish-eye portrait of *Architeuthis dux*, the world's biggest squid - good luck, if you ever see one - a cephalopod shot makes a great inclusion in the portfolio.

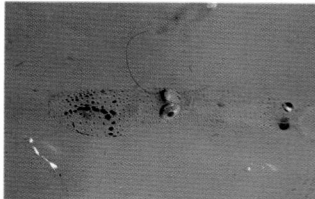

Just before birth, little eyes can
be seen through the egg cases.r
Sepioteuthis lessoniana
105mm / f22 , 1/ 125
Kelasey, Nth Sulawesi

Mating dance of Sepio squids
after sunset.
Sepioteuthis lessoniana
60mm / f11 , 1/ 60
Kelasey, Nth Sulawesi

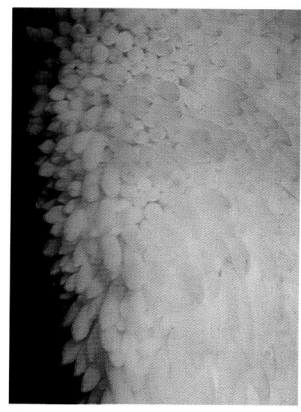

Over three nights, the squid laid these
egg 'capsules' on a mooring line.
Sepioteuthis lessoniana
60mm / f8 , 1/ 60
Kelasey, Nth Sulawesi

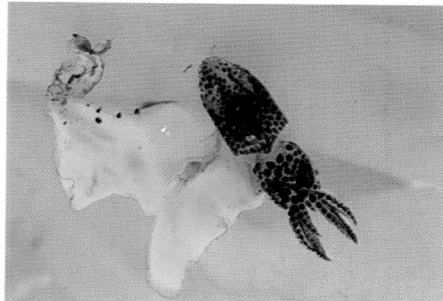

Little hatchlings are capable
of changing colours and
squirting ink immediately after birth.
Sepioteuthis lessoniana
105mm / f22 , 1/ 125
Kelasey, Nth Sulawesi

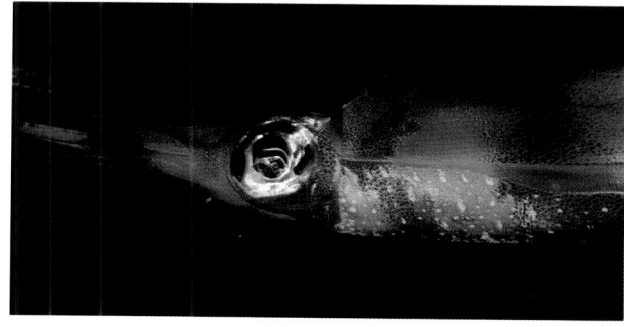

This male has put on
his mating colour
to attract the girls.
Sepioteuthis lessoniana
60mm / f16 , 1/ 60
Kelasey, Nth Sulawesi

SEA MOSSES PHYLUM BRYOZOA

Sea mosses or bryozoans get a rough deal. When they are not completely ignored, they are often mistaken for some kind of a reef plant or sponge. There are, in fact, more than 4,000 species of bryozoan distributed worldwide from tropical reefs to the Antarctic. All receive little or no attention from snorkellers, scuba divers or even the scientific community - after all you can't really get famous researching a subject that doesn't even make good dinner conversation. Bryozoans never win the popularity contest or appear on the front cover of magazines.

VISIBLY INVISIBLE

Bryozoans or zooids are seldom seen, but these seldomly observed animals are actually elegant, resembling decorative lace or ribbon flowers, and are found everywhere under ledges, between corals and sponges, along walls and shady crevices, and on ship hulls and jetties. Bryozoans are sessile colonial animals, but each individual within a colony is independent of the others, living in an armour of extremely minute calcareous or membranous material visible only through the lens of a microscope. The body plan of these tiny animals is complex, with a well-developed digestive system, mouth, stomach and anus, a retractable feeding structure called a lophophore, and a bilaterally symmetrical body without head.

FEEDING UTENSILS

Zooids are suspension feeders, which means that they munch on planktonic goodies home-delivered to them by passing water. Their lophophores are specialised feeding organs comprised of a mouth fringed with a tentacle-like moustache coated with cilia which is used to filter food out of the water. The lophophore can revolve to face into the current, optimising the number of food organisms bumping into the tentacles. The movement of cilia then pushes the catch toward the mouth. Positioning your anus just next to your mouth may not seem hygiénic to us, but it is a very efficient arrangement for a sedentary animal. Food ingested through the mouth is moved through a U-shaped digestive tract by means of cilia and any waste products are ejected through the other end, the anus.

MAKING MOSSES

Moss reproduces by budding into another moss, as well as by sexual reproduction. Most zooids produce both eggs and sperm which can be shed into a hollow cavity where fertilisation takes place. Once the eggs hatch, the newly born larvae are expelled in the blue where they lead a perilous life before they are ready to settle down on a hard surface to develop into adults. Few survive. Most of them fall straight into the fronds of other suspension feeders. Even as adults, bryozoans are tantalizing meals for nudibranchs and spider crabs, some of which feed exclusively on them.

HOMEMADE REPELLENT

Like other sessile animals, bryozoans are always in danger of having the larvae of other animals settle on them. If these larvae survive, they can eventually grow over the bryozoan colony. To combat possible intruders, bryozoans produce their own toxic chemical repellent. Bryozoans also possess specialised little zooids, modified with pincers, to pluck off any persistent larvae before they have the chance to develop.

Triphyllozoon inornatum
60 mm, f16 1/125
Mabul, Malaysia

Tricellaria / Scrupocellaria sp.
60 mm, f16 1/125
Pulisang, Nth Sulawesi

Canda sp.
60mm f22 1/60
Alor, Indonesia

CRUSTACEANS - PHYLUM ARTHROPODA

Most of us have an affinity with the phylum *Arthropoda*. We eat them, we live with them, we kill them, we fear them and yet our knowledge of crustaceans usually only goes as far as the blue swimmer crabs, lobsters, bugs and shrimp that we throw on our BBQ. The *Sub-Phylum Crustacea*, belongs to the *Arthropoda*, which includes the land-dwelling insects, spiders, scorpions, millipedes, bugs and centipedes, and is the most dominant phylum of the animal kingdom. Out of the estimated 750,000 described species of *Arthropoda*, only about 30,000 are crustaceans of the sea.

Crustaceans are amazingly diverse with regard to their shapes, colour, body functions and lifestyles. One of the most incredible features of crustaceans that should be envied by a few males of the human kind belongs to the barnacles. Those little fellows that live on rocky shores are able to extend their penis up to 30 times their body size to reach their female friends next door during sexual reproduction.

ARMOURED INSECTS OF THE SEA

Most crustaceans are easily recognisable with the presence of a rigid armour-like outer casing (exoskeleton) composed of calcium carbonate. The underlying protected, bilaterally symmetrical, soft body is divided into segments. Crustaceans do however have a price to pay for such formidable protection. As growth is continuous during their life cycle, they periodically outgrow their body armour and it is necessary for them to shed (moult) and replace the shell at regular intervals. Just prior to moulting, these 'insects' of the sea recycle part of their shells by absorbing the calcium, while a new shell is being developed. When the old shell is finally shed, the new coat of armour is still relatively soft. Therefore, to avoid predators, it is necessary for them to seek refuge in burrows or crevices. Some species will eat part of the old outer casing as a calcium supplement to harden their new armour, making use of a resource that would otherwise be wasted.

Crustaceans have a well developed head, nervous system and sensory organs and some of their kin are known to posses incredibly acute eyesight. Their body is divided into three sections - head, thorax and abdomen. The head and thorax is often fused as the cephalothorax, and the back tail section is the abdomen. One feature of crustaceans, as with all arthropods, is their jointed limbs, with internal muscles, designed for moving in all directions. Apart from locomotion, their limbs perform other important functions acting as feeders, touch sensors, chemical receptors, respiratory devices, as well as being used for aggression and defence. A conspicuous characteristic of all crustaceans is the presence of two pairs of antennae on their heads (as opposed to a single pair or sometimes none in other arthropods), and some have pincer-like claws. The diet of crustaceans varies in content from bacteria, plankton, sediments, suspended organisms, algae, molluscs, fish and worms to other crustaceans and carrion.

Dark finger reef crab
Etisus dentatus
60mm / f11 , 1/ 60
Nain, Nth Sulawesi

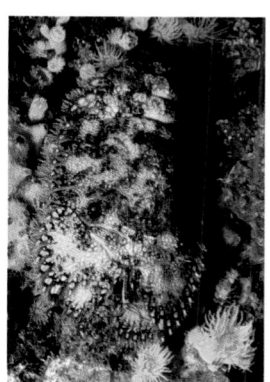

Painted rock lobster
Panulirus versicolor
24mm / f11 , 1/ 60
Mahahetang, Nth Sulawesi

Slipper lobster
Parribacus antarcticus
60mm / f16 , 1/ 60
Bunaken, Nth Sulawesi

Spider crab
Schizophrys aspera
60mm / f16 , 1/ 60
Pulisang, Nth Sulawesi

Ten Crusty Legs

The majority of crustaceans we encounter on coral reefs are decapods, literally meaning "ten legs". Shrimp, crabs and lobsters are all decapods. Apart from distinctively different shapes, the major difference between shrimp, lobsters and crabs is that the abdomen of shrimp and lobsters is muscular and extends from the back of the head, whereas in crabs, it is flexed forward under the body. Crabs and shrimp are favourite menu items among fishes and other bigger invertebrates such as squid and cuttlefish. Crustaceans therefore live "underground", in holes, burrows and crevices during the day. After dark they emerge on the reef to forage for shellfish, tiny reef organisms and other reef "tit bits".

Health and Relaxation Clinics Run by Shrimp

Nature has its own ways of looking after its not-so-healthy folks. Some brightly coloured shrimp of the genus *Stenopus* and genus *Lysmata* set up permanent "stations" on the reef to service a clientele of damselfishes, groupers, triggerfishes, surgeonfishes and large Napoleon wrasse. At these "clinics", the patients hover stationary, while teams of shrimp fearlessly clamber all over their client's body, mouth and gills. These "cleaner" shrimp tend to the patient by plucking off parasites and get paid in kind by feeding on the mucus coat of their client. This is one of the many mutually beneficial arrangements among animals of the coral reef which plays a vital role in the ecological well being of the reef (see "Tenancy Agreements", p144).

Making Crabs and Shrimp

As with most higher forms of animals, decapods each have either male or female organs. Some of the most elaborate courtship rituals and sexual behavioural patterns of all marine animals are indulged in by crustaceans and may last from a few hours to an overnight affair (see "Stomatopoda", p114). After receiving sperm from the male, fertilisation occurs. The female then carries the fertilised eggs on her abdomen until they hatch to be released into the planktonic realm. Some female lobsters are known to store excess sperm on their chests for later use. Once the hatchlings are freed, they go through progressive stages of development before settling on the reef to assume the life of an adult crustacean.

More about Crabs

There are two main types of crustaceans popularly known as crabs, the anomurans and the brachyurans, in general, those with an obvious tail section and those without. One of the most often encountered members of the tailed crabs are of the superfamily *Paguroidae*, or hermit crabs. Unlike most crabs who need to hide after the moulting process, the hermit crab simply finds a larger empty shell to move into.

Other well known anomurans or tailed crabs are those found living in anemones, sponges, sea cucumbers and coral which are often referred to as Porcelain crabs (*Porcellanidae*). Squat lobsters with their oval bodies and pointed beaks living among feather stars (*Echinoderm*) are also anomurans (*Galatheidae*).

Anemone shrimp
Periclimenes holthuisi
105mm / f22 , 1/ 60
Bunaken. Nth Sulawesi

Palaemonid shrimp
Leander plumosus
105mm / f22 , 1/ 60
Ruang, Nth Sulawesi

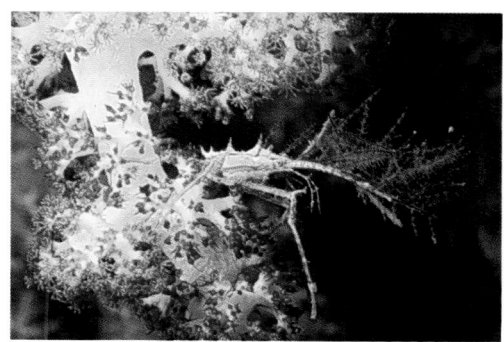

Decorator arrow crab -
this has hydroids for defense .
Hyastenus bispinosus
105mm / f22 , 1/ 60
Bunaken. Nth Sulawesi

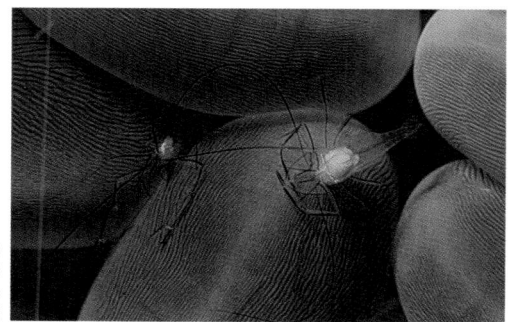

Bubble coral shrimp
Vic philippinensis
105mm / f22 , 1/ 125
Bunaken, Nth Sulawesi

TRUE CRABS

True crabs are the crabs we know, yes ... the one's that have pincers and walk sideways. Brachyurans do not have an obvious tail as their abdomen is folded under the thorax, their antennae are small and their first pair of limbs have developed into strong pincers or chelipeds. They have a flattened body and their carapace is fused with a rigid ventral plate. The crab most people are familiar with is also the one we eat, and is of the family of *Portunidae* which is comprised of swimmer crabs and the most well known mud or mangrove crabs (*Scylla serrata*).

Species of true crabs have a diverse range of sizes and habitats. They range from a crab of just a few millimetres which lives in the planktonic layer to giants weighing 10 kgs/33lbs (*Pseudocarcinus gigas*) which live at depths in excess of 100 metres.

Another type of crab which we frequently encounter is the crab which runs around on sandy beaches and mud flats. The ghost and fiddler crabs (*Ocypodidae*) are easily distinguished by their long, erect eye stalks and easily traced by their excavated burrows and piles of sand left along the beach. A family of crab frequently seen on the coral reef, especially at night, is the *Xanthidae* or Black-finger coral crabs. Most of these crabs are recognised by their black tipped claws despite variations in their body form and colour.

STRANGE LOOKING OR DECORATOR CRAB

Spider or decorator crabs are some of best disguised and most decorative artists of the reef. For camouflage and protection, some species simply throw a piece of sponge twice their size on their back (*Lauridromia dehaani*), while others carefully snip a selection of tunicates, sponges, anemones and hydroids (*Camposcia retusa*) and carefully place them on their body and legs.

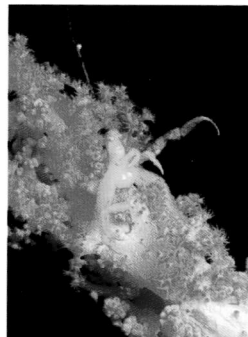

Butterscotch spider crab
possibly new sp
105mm, f32 1/60 .
Alor, Indonesia

Porcelain commensal crab
Porcellanella sp
105mm, f22 1/125
Derawan, Kalimantan

Humback cleaner shrimp
Lysmata amboinensis
105mm / f22, 1/60
Dondola, Sulawesi

Cleaner shrimps at work on moray eel
Leandrites cyrtohynchus
60mm / f16, 1/60
Togian, Sulawesi

Snapping goby shrimp
Alpheus djiboutensis
105mm / f22, 1/60
Komodo, Indonesia

Hermit crab
Dardanus megistos
60mm / f11, 1/60
Mabul, Malaysia

Anemone decorated crab
Dardanus pedunculatus
60mm / f11, 1/60
Kelasey, Nth Sulawesi

NOT A DECAPOD

Other crustaceans that are not decapods are simply referred to as non-decapods. Rather famous as shore animals, though not very crustacean-like, barnacles are in fact modified crustaceans that live standing on their "heads", using their feet to sweep plankton into their mouths. The typically jointed crustacean limbs are modified to form feeding cirri. These appendages are positioned outside the barnacles' shells and the beating movement creates a current to draw food into their mouths.

Most species of barnacles are hermaphrodites, but cross-fertilisation is required for procreation of their species. Each barnacle is responsible for impregnating its neighbour with its penis, which can be extended up to 30 times the length of its body if necessary. Fertilised eggs hatch into planktonic larvae, which do not resemble the parent at all, but are easily distinguishable as a crustacean. The free-living crustacean larvae go through a feeding period before developing into a non-feeding period that is specially reserved for the vital task of habitat selection. When the final stage occurs, the larvae must settle down, head first, to develop into a barnacle, after which it will spend its entire life upside down. Some species of barnacles bore into shells and corals while others attach to the abdomens of crabs and other crustaceans living parasitically, or actually living inside their host and feeding on its body tissues.

Other non-decapods are mainly very small microscopic animals. They represent the bulk of drifting plankton and include isopods, copepods, ostracods, mysids and amphipods. Their importance to the ecology of the coral reef cannot be over emphasised. As part of the food chain, feeding on single-celled plants, they are the food source of many invertebrates and juvenile fishes. The most common isopod visible on coral reefs are the parasitic fish lice (*Cymothoidae*), measuring up to 3-4 cm long. These flattened, segmented 'bugs' are often seen behind the head of damselfishes and hawkfishes.

CRAB PICTURES

Crustaceans make interesting pictures, especially behavioural shots. Most of them are nocturnal, so a strong strobe attached with a powerful modelling light is required for ease of photography. As they are generally small and shy, a 105mm lens is recommended, but beware, they are a real test for patience. They have a bad habit of hopping away just as you depress the shutter.

Cleaner shrimp
Leandrites cyrtorhynchus
105mm / f22 , 1/ 60
Taguladang, Nth Sulawesi

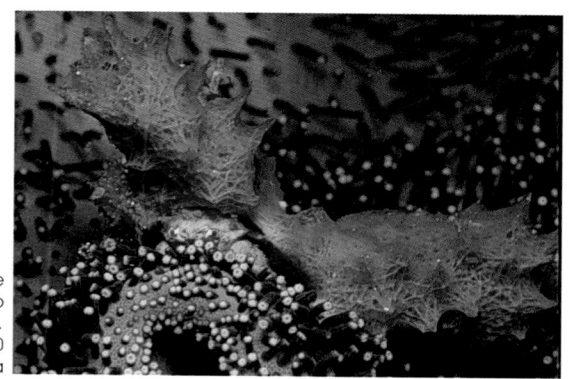

Sponge
camouflaged crab
possibly Dromidiopsis sp.
105mm / f22 , 1/ 60
Alor, Indonesia

Fish Lice Isopoda
Cymathoidae sp.
105mm / f16 , 1/ 60
Tukang Besi, Indonesia

Squat Lobster
Xenocarcinus conicus.
105mm / f22 , 1/ 125
Derawan, Indonesia

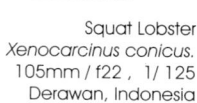

'Micomac' Decorator crab
Camposcia retusa
60mm / f16 , 1/ 60
Derawan, Indonesia

Mantis Shrimp
Phylum Crustacea - Order Stomatopoda

The life and times of the mantis shrimp conjures up images of a Jurassic Park creature transplanted into the medieval days of glory. The ability of these prehistoric solitary warriors, in blazing colours, to cruise through a life of fighting carnage, and occasional lustful servicing by willing mates, has earned them a section of their own in this book.

Mantis shrimps or stomatopods are an ancient and unsociable band of crustaceans whose attributes set them apart in their environment. These animals view life through super-visionary bug eyes and exist unashamedly in a universe of aggression and intense copulative fervour. There are 400 known stomatopod species found in shallow tropical and warm temperate waters. This has enabled data to be collected on many individuals.

Quick Draw Claws of the Deep

Through concomitant evolution, mantis shrimps have emerged with two unique characteristics that work in conjunction to establish their preying prowess. The mantis shrimp's most notable endowment is its heavy armament of deadly raptorial claws on a lobster-like body, resembling those of a Raptorsaurus from the Jurassic era. In response to predatory behaviour, these oversized feeding and fighting appendages have evolved structurally into two groups - smashers and spearers. The taxonomy of stomatopods has been revised dividing them into 5 superfamilies.

The superfamily of *Gonodactylidea* are smashers and some spearers, *Lysiosquillidea* consists mostly of spearers with some smashers, whereas *Squilloidea* and *Bathysquillidae* are both exclusively spearers. The fifth group *Erythrosquilloidea* contains only a single species which is a spearer. The distal section (or dactyls) of the raptorial appendages are blade shaped, and either armed with spines which have barbs at the tip (spearers), or unarmed but re-enforced with a heavily calcified and greatly inflated heel (smashers). It is these predatory claws and their function that bear a strong resemblance to the terrestrial preying mantis, from which the mantis shrimp acquires its common name.

Spearers possess deadly-looking spines (2 - 20+ in number) on the last joint of their raptors, turning these limbs into deadly and effective predatory spears. They build burrows and wait in ambush at the entrance for their soft-bodied prey (such as fishes and shrimps). When a target is in sight, the spearer lashes out with its weaponry in a precise upward spearing motion with an impressive velocity of 10 metres per second. It is one of the fastest animal movements to impale a victim ever recorded (4 8 milliseconds). Once prey is rendered immobile, the spearer hooks it inwards on its jointed limb and begins the process of consumption pulling the prey towards its mouthparts and ripping it to pieces with its hooked maxillipeds.

Smasher mantis shrimp
Gonodactylus smithii
105mm / f22 , 1/ 60

Spearer mantis shrimp,
probably a new
Lysiosquilla sp.
60mm / f16, 1/ 60
Kelasey, Nth Sulawesi

Smasher mantis shrimp, note the calcified
heel on the raptorial claws
Gonodactylus scyallarus
105mm / f11 , 1/ 60
Derawan, East Kalimantan

Raptorial claw of the
spearer mantis shrimp,
Lysiosquilla sp.
60mm / f16, 1/ 60
Kelasey, Nth Sulawesi

Smashers possess a large and heavily calcified heel on their raptorial claws which makes an incredibly efficient bludgeoning weapon. Smashers live in coral or rock crevices where they lie in wait, seeking out crabs and cone shells which they physically stalk. They will either stage a surprise attack, or back their victims into tight spaces. Once a victim is within range a smasher will raise its giant raptor and smash the heel down on the victim's shell. The force of this action is extraordinarily powerful, and in the larger species has been likened to that of a small calibre bullet. Individuals of the brightly coloured larger species *Odontodactylus scyllarus* (7cm) have been known to break the walls of glass aquariums with their strike. Obviously, they are not good house pets.

SUPER-VISIONARY POWER

Another key to the powers of this ancient predator is its possession of incredible visionary abilities. As stomatopods cannot turn their heads, their ability to independently rotate each eyeball in a full 360-degree scan is a necessary element of their survival as supreme predators.

Mantis shrimps have pairs of compound eyes mounted on movable stalks. Each eye is made up of 10,000 visual elements (ommatidia). Although the visual fields of ommatidia overlap, especially in the areas of highest activity, each ommatidium views the world through a separate lens capable of pointing in different directions. The concave effect produced enables the animal to have binocular, and in some cases trinocular vision (the effect being that when one of the mantis shrimp's eyes is looking at you, it is actually seeing you from more than one perspective similar to permanently viewing the world through a primitive kaleidoscope).

Looking into a mantis shrimp's eye you will see three black spots or pseudopupils, each comprised of thousands of ommatidia pointing directly at you. Moving to the side, only two pseudopupils are visible. Effectively, when a mantis shrimp focuses both eyes on a target, it is said to have hexnocular vision. These "super-visionary powers" have evolved concomitantly with the stomatopod's rapid raptorial strike abilities, giving this animal one of the most effective prey and predator range-finding systems ever documented.

ARMOURED WARRIOR

The mantis shrimp is not only a ferocious hunter, but a fierce fighter as well. By nature, fiercely protective of its home, it will participate in battles with its own kind in intense territorial disputes one of the oldest stories in the history of nature. Unless there is vehement competition for dwelling space, killing is rare in these brawls, with the motive, more often than not, being to dominate rather than to destroy.

Though death is rare in combat, injuries can occur and it can become a slight inconvenience when the raptorial appendage is severely damaged. Mantis shrimps cannot just shed their limbs (as crabs can) but must tear them off and wait for new limbs to regenerate over the next two or three moults.

Gonodactylus chiragra
105mm / f22, 1/ 60
Tderawan, East Kalimantan

Lysiosquilla sp.
105mm / f22, 1/ 60
Kelasey, Nth Sulawesi

EYES ON A STALK

Note the three black spots or pseudopupils, each comprised of thousands of ommatidia pointing directly at you. Moving to the side, only two pseudopupils are visible. Effectively, when a mantis shrimp focuses both eyes on a target, it is said to have hexnocular vision.

Gonodactylus scyllarus
105mm / f22, 1/ 60
Kelasey, Nth Sulawesi

After repeatedly playing with this Lysiosquilla spearer over a period of one year, we documented this one having the ability to learn and play games. 60mm / f16, 1/ 60
Kelasey, Nth Sulawesi

INSATIABLE SEX

Stomatopods are generally solitary dwellers with only *Lysiosquilla* forming monogamo pairs and there is little evidence of the formation of commensal or symbio relationships other than a few small species found living with sand dwelling tube worn Maybe it is this otherwise isolated lifestyle that explains why, when it comes to matir time, they have such an exhausting time in the pursuit of fascinating, even if at tim extremely aggressive sexual indulgence. Males are sexually insatiable, except direc after a previous encounter, therefore it is specifically the female's selection th determines mating couples. The female is very particular in her choice of mate, ar males embark on an exhaustive "door-knocking" process, calling on female chambe offering their service.

Once a mating couple is established a bizarre courtship ensues, involving aggressi behaviour including ritualistic displays of threat, and continuous battle-like striking o and shielding. After much showcasing and simulated battering the couple eventuc become conditioned to one another, and the two become entwined. Once th female is sufficiently aroused the male is allowed close enough to inject his sperm.

This ritual continues for up to one week, probably in an attempt to ensure that no otr male mates with the female. However, the path of this true love does not run smooth 1 very much longer, with the female gradually losing interest and becoming mo aggressive with her mate, eventually violently evicting him from her burrow. The eg are then laid and remain with the female until the new breed of stomatopods hatc Once the first larval stages are complete the young take off on their own, swimmir away into the big blue.

Brutal predators, aggressive lovers and formidable fighters, the creed of survival stomatopod society seems to be "fight and be fought". Nothing, it seems, comes these creatures without a struggle - symbolic in many ways of the state of many speci around the planet.

BRING LOTS OF AMMUNITION AND SHOOT FAST

This one you will have fun, as mantis shrimps are the ultimate test for your skills ar patience. Use a 105mm lens and be prepared to spend the entire dive on one subje Approach with caution, for obvious reasons, you will need to shoot fast!

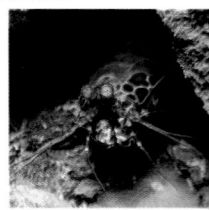

Generally very timid, smashers
generally prefer to shy away from divers.
Gonodactylus scyallarus
105mm / f11 , 1/ 60

This spearer is having
fun trying to feast on
spawning worms.
Lysiosquilla sp.
60mm / f11 , 1/ 60
Biaro, Nth Sulawesi

Caught out in the open,
busy stalking for food.
105mm / f11 , 1/ 60
Kelasey, Nth Sulawesi

This one is lucky,
hauling a prey in
for a feast.
Gonodactylus smithii
105mm / f11 , 1/ 60

SEA STARS PHYLUM ECHINODERMATA

CLASS ASTEROIDEA

Sea stars are gentle, somewhat not too smart, harmless animals; at least this is the image promoted by marine aquariums encouraging kids to feel and learn about the sea by touching these five-armed, symmetrical, seemingly defenceless stars. BU parents, beware!! After reading this, you and your toddlers might want to head for the nearest hiding hole the next time a sea star is in sight.

These animals feed by thrusting their stomach out of their mouths and digesting the prey outside their body. There is no safe place to hide, not even in hard calcareou shells. A gap of 0.1mm is wide enough to allow their stomach to penetrate and finish th job. Relative to body size, we might seem like Gulliver to these star-shaped animals. Bu imagine your hand being digested by an overturned stomach right in front of your eyes.

Sea stars deserve more respect. They are often referred to as starfish. Sea stars are no related to, nor do they even remotely look like, fish. Sea stars are members of the *Phylum Echinoderm*, literally meaning "spiny skins", which also includes the clan of se cucumbers, urchins, crinoids and brittle stars. Another strictly aquatic animal, sea sta emerged on earth some 500 million years ago and today there are about 1,60 species, mostly living in shallow coastal water and coral reefs.

Sea stars and their clan are easily recognised by a radially symmetrical body, with five o more arms radiating from a central disc. The body of a sea star has a distinct top an bottom, but it does not have distinct right and left sides.   The body plan of mo echinoderms is unique amongst complex multi-cellular animals. Their body plan orientated around a central point. Humans and most other animals are said to b bilaterally symmetrical, having a body of mirrored left and right sections. Sea stars ar composed of five or more equal segments, each comprised of a clone set of intern organs. The centrally located mouth is on the bottom (oral) side of the animal and th anus, connected by stomach and intestine, is on the top (aboral) side.

Sea stars have tube feet with sucker pads Spiderman would have been impressed. typical animal has two or four rolls of hundreds and thousands of these feet in th grooves on the underside of its arms. Locomotion is by means of a remarkable wate vascular system, common to all echinoderms. Water is pumped into the system throug a sieved plate on the upper surface, transferred to each individual arm by intern canals and then conveyed to the tubed feet. Hydrostatic pressure inflates and deflate the system, resulting in slow but sturdy movement, enabling them to climb vertical wal or to move upside down in caverns.

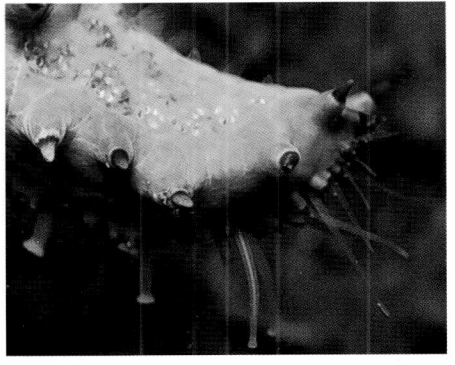

Hydrostatic pressure
enables sea stars to move
with their tube feet.
105mm / f11 , 1/ 60

Frainti sea star
Nardoa frianti
60mm / f16 , 1/ 60
Lembata, Indonesia

Striking Monli sea star
Fromia monilis
60mm / f11 , 1/ 60
Kelasey, Nth Sulawesi

gathering of Knobby sea stars
Protoreaster nodosus
14 / f8 , 1/ 60
Manadp Tua, Nth Sulawesi

How Stars are Born

Would you believe that some sea stars bear live young sea stars! But only in the colder water species, like that of *Patiriella vivipara* found in Tasmania. Without obvious sexual genitals, sex is not very exciting - mature males and females simply release eggs and sperm into the water column. Fertilised eggs spend a span of time in the water column as bilaterally symmetrical beings before settling to metamorphose into little stars. Very few larvae survive. However, sea stars are well known for their regeneration power. A small fragment can develop into a whole new adult. Some species can reproduce simply by splitting in half and regenerating missing parts to form two new complete bodies. This art of regeneration is also used to replace physical damage suffered from predation and many species can survive even after loosing half their body.

Sea Stars Secrets

How do slow moving sea stars prevent other organisms from making their homes on them? This is the secret of the stars, known only among their kin and a few specialised biologists. Lodged on their aboral surface are minute, jaw-like structures called pedicellariae. With a sort of parrot beak, the pedicellariae, when stimulated by touch (such as the settling of barnacle larvae), will instantaneously grab the living daylights out of the intruder.

Turning Stomachs Inside Out

This is the best description of the feeding behaviour of sea stars. They literally thrust their stomachs out of their mouth and digest their victim externally. Their diet of sea star varies between species. They may feed on sponges, bryozoans, ascidians, molluscs corals or bottom detritus. Species that prey on bivalves are able to pry the shells apart by exerting force on the muscles which hold the two shells together. Once the muscles are weakened, the sea star will insert its stomach through the extremely small opening and cover the prey entirely with its digestive organ. When the meal is finished, the stomach is withdrawn back into the body. Reports indicate that even if a mussel wrapped in wire, so that it cannot be opened, the sea star *Pisaster orhraceus* is still able to digest away the animal in its entirety. Crown-of-thorns sea stars (*Acanthaster planci*) feed mainly on hard coral polyps. They are notorious for wiping out reefs in the Indo Pacific, including those of the Australian Great Barrier Reef system. However, recent research shows that outbreaks of *Acanthaster* have occurred for at least the last 10,000 years or more on the Great Barrier Reef. The reefs have survived those infestations and will probably survive the next.

Pictures of Sea Stars

Though a gathering of sea stars makes for interesting wide perspective pictures, stars of the sea are generally not award-winning material. However, those that live among the stars are. On most echinoderms, if you probe carefully, you will find many interesting symbionts living among the fronds of the stars, including worms, squat lobsters, shrimps crabs, clingfishes and tiny cardinalfishes, sometimes mouthing a brood of eggs (see "Tenancy agreements", p 144). A 105mm lens with twin strobes is essential and works well with TTL set-up.

Regeneration power went overtime, the star on the left
has added one arm too many. Linkia sea star generally have 5 arms.
Linckialae vigata 60mm / f11 , 1/ 60, Tioman, Malaysia / Alor Indonesia

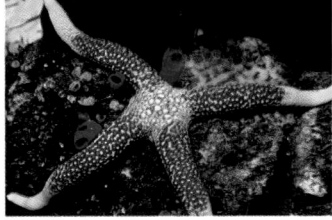

This star is quite
happy to live
with just 4 arms.
Fromia sp.
60mm / f16 , 1/ 60
Kelasey, Nth Sulawesi

Luzon sea star
Echinaster luzonicas
60mm / f16 , 1/ 125
Davao, Phillipines

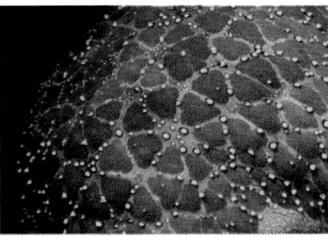

Pincushion sea star
Culcita novaeguineae
60mm / f16 , 1/ 125
Muiron Island, WA, Australia

A Crown of thorns completely wrapped
around to devour the plate coral.
Acanthaster planci 60mm / f22 , 1/ 60
Dondola, Nth Sulawesi

A reef devastated by Crown of thorns in 1992,
Acanthaster planci 24mm / f5.6 , 1/ 60
Swain Reef, GBR, Australia

FEATHER STARS - PHYLUM ECHINODERMATA

Feather stars are the Supermodels of the sea. The prettiest of all sea stars, they stand out prominently, waving their delicate arms, but they have no brains or, rather, a lack thereof. They have small, cute, central bodies surrounded by five to 200 arms (always a multiple of five), which have fine lateral branches giving them the feathery appearance. The most common feather stars found on the coral reef have between 10 and 20 arms. Feather stars, alias crinoids, belong to the *Class Crinoidea* of the *Phylum Echinodermata* and are related to sea stars, sea urchins, sea cucumbers and brittle stars. Their common traits include a radially symmetrical body, tube feet and numerous arms projecting from a central disc.

Feather stars are highly visible characters on coral reefs. They come in some of the brightest colour combinations from crimson red, metallic blue, green, canary yellow, aqua blue and snow white to bronze, silver and gold. Using special "bird-claw-like" appendages or "cirri" on the undersides of their bodies, they love to perch on the highest points of gorgonian fans, sponges, or tall corals, exposing themselves to the strong currents which convey rich planktonic nutrients. As they are filter feeders, their mouth is on the upper side. The anus, like the sea star, is also on the upper surface but is positioned on an elevated cone.

FALLING STARS

Coral reef crinoids are generally moderate in size, with a span across the stretched out arms varying from 30 - 60cm. Unlike other echinoderms, feather stars do not use their tube feet for locomotion. If they need to move, they generally do so by slowly and deliberately grasping the substrate with their cirri. For a quick getaway, perhaps to escape predators, or to search for richer "pastures", some release their cirri's grip and using a peculiarly beautiful undulatory motion of their arms to lift themselves up into the water and "swim" for short distances. The swimming is undirectional as the feather stars lack eyes to see where they are going. This results in random movement. Like a falling star, a feather star wanders in the blue for while and essentially stops where it lands.

SEX WITH FEATHERY BEING

Sex among male and female feather stars is straightforward. Sperm and ova are released into the sea according to nature's biological clock where fertilisation occurs to produce non-feeding larvae. After a short planktonic existence, at metamorphosis, the larvae turn into miniature sea lilies (crinoid-like with a stalk), and attach themselves to the substrate. After a brief period of growth, the stalks break off and a small version of an adult crinoid emerges to live on the reef.

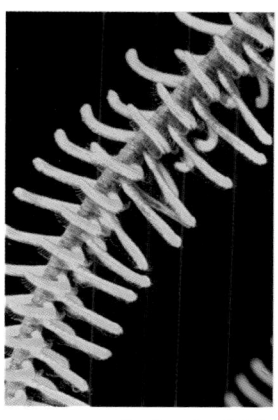

Featherstar details
Comanthina schlegeli
105mm / f22, 1/ 125

Bird-like claw appendages
60mm / f22, 1/ 60
Layang Layang, Malaysia

Comanthina sp.
60mm / f11, 1/ 60
Bunaken, Nth Sulawesi

HIGHLY SELECTIVE DIETS

Feather stars are exceptionally "picky" about their diet.. They are difficult to please and consequently often starve to death in captivity. Unlike other suspension feeders which passively filter food from the water, somehow sorting it out after collection, crinoids actively select each meal. Presumably their choices are based on the flavour, composition, size and density of each item. Each of their feathery arms have numerous side branches called pinnules with a food conveyor belt in the middle (grooves) lined with a row of tube feet on each side.

Crinoids use these tube feet in a very unique method to collect food. The feet work in teams of six. Each team is divided into two groups of three feet facing each other across the food belt. Each group of three consists of a long, medium and short tube foot and each individual plays a specific role in feeding. When a long tube foot on one side catches an acceptable food item (eg, larvae), it flicks, knocking the item towards the middle foot on other side - just like a football session. The middle foot flexes to knock the item across to the short tube foot on the original side, which in turn kicks the item into the food belt where it is conveyed to the mouth by sticky mucus. The mucus on the feather star's feathery arms is nature's version of Velcro. Divers with bad buoyancy control often return from a dive with half the reef's crinoid population on their wetsuits.

Though crinoids are primarily nocturnal animals, shying away from bright lights, they are also opportunistic animals. It is not uncommon to find them in full display during the day, hanging on to various substrates to feed in vigorous currents. Along the wall of Kalabahi channel, in Alor, Indonesia, where huge tidal movement occurs twice a day, I found probably the densest population of crinoids in the world - more than 100 individuals in a single square meter.

Though their bright colours may indicate the presence of toxins to deter potential predators, their habit of living in the open subjects them to some persistent predation. The fact that feather stars have the ability to regenerate lost arms quickly means that they actually provide a renewable resource for their fish predators.

PICTURES OF THOSE THAT MINGLE WITH STARS

The dense jungles of crinoids are favoured as home for an array of marine animals. Living among their fronds are clingfishes, squat lobsters, crinoid shrimps and brittle stars. The feather star not only provides shelter and mobility for these commensal creatures, but also a steady supply of free meals delivered along their food conveyor belts (see "Tenancy agreements", p144). It is not easy to capture pictures of these symbionts, but with a little encouragement you might get lucky. Try a gentle tickle on the cirri, it might give such pleasure to the animal that it causes it to relax and open up its arms to show off a house guest. If this doesn't work, don't manhandle the animal, move on to one that can be more easily aroused.

Catching nutrients from tidal currents.
24mm / f11 , 1/ 60
Maldives

Varied of Oxycomanthus sp.
24mm / f11, 1/ 60
Ambon, Indonesia

Swimming to
'greener pastures'
Stephanometra sp.
60mm / f16, 1/ 125

BRITTLE & BASKET STARS PHYLUM ECHINODERMATA

Lurking within the dark chambers and corridors of the sea are multi-armed creatures scurrying from mount to mount. Creepy crawlies with whip-like arms lined with brittle spikes, they move with serpentine swiftness, waiting to trap their next victim with a slush of gluey mucus. These cryptic animals are aptly named snake stars, serpent stars or brittle stars. Though akin to the sea stars, they don't look friendly and share only a few characteristics. In fact, besides having arms and a mouth located beneath a central disc, they have little in common. Their arms are highly flexible, composed of a series of solid skeletal segments resembling muscles and ligaments.

BRITTLE STARS - ORDER OPHIURIDA

Like all echinoderms, brittle stars have a water vascular system. However, instead of having a locomotive function, it is used primarily for feeding. Their arms bear tube feet, without suckers, which emit sticky mucus to trap organisms and detritus. The brittle star's mouth, located under its central disk, also serves the role of an anus. By a vigorous rowing action with their arms, the brittle star moves with incredible swiftness, disappearing beneath rocks, shells, corals, sand or mud. As part of their defense system, they can autotomize (detach) a part of, or an entire appendage, when seized by a fish or crab. The brittle star's regeneration process, involving wound repair and new arm formation, is achieved in only 12 days; although it may take up to 300 days of somatic growth to reach final weight and length.

SERPENTS, BASKETS AND YOUNG - ORDER PHRYNOPHIURIDA

Serpent stars (*Asteroschematidae*) are more complex cousins of the brittle star and are often seen wound around gorgonian fans and black coral trees in a snake-like fashion. Basket stars (*Gorgonocephalidae)* easily recognised by their multi-branched basket-like arms which differ from from serpent stars, are like baskets on the reef when they emerge to feed at night. The basket-textured arms are effective "nets" for trapping a variety of organisms. Knowledge of their sexual behaviour is as delphic as knowledge of their lifestyle, but it would not be wrong to assume that these echinoderms reproduce sexually by shedding sperm and ova or laying eggs, brooding young within the body or reproducing asexually by cleaving themselves.

CELEBRATE THE SERPENTS

Of late, pictures of brittle stars have made the front covers of magazines and at least one has won international awards. Use a 60mm lens and shoot them against a dark background. They make interesting enigmatic portraits.

Serpent star in the day
Astrobrachian adhaerens.
24mm / f11, 1/ 60
Bunaken, Nth Sulawesi

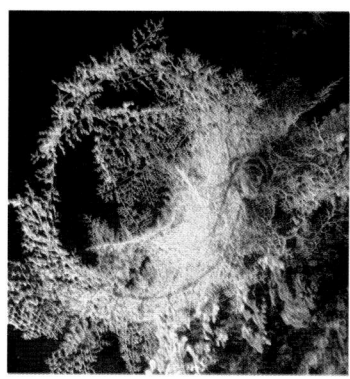

Bastket Star
Astroboa nuda
24mm / f8, 1/ 60
Great Barrier Reef, Australia

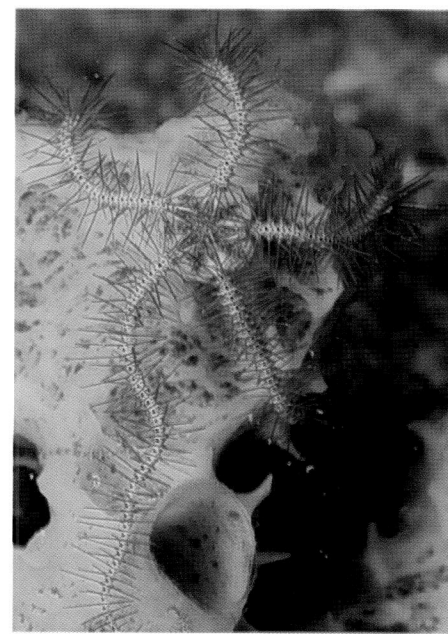

Brittle star
Ophiothrix sp.
105mm / f22 , 1/ 60
Semilan Island, Thailand

Sea Urchins Phylum Echinodermata

Human beings should be envious of sea urchins. They have been sent to space, not as astronauts, but for biological research into the effect of that environment on their sexual fertilisation process and embryo development. There might be a new generation of space urchins lurking in the corridors of the universe. Starship Enterprise beware!

Sea urchins may put white mice out of work in the laboratory. Lately, urchins' eggs have been employed to provide insight into the beginning of life and have been studied in conjunction with human fertilisation research. Marine laboratories all over the world are turning to testing specimens of sea urchins eggs for compounds to cure and prevent cancer, AIDS and other biological viruses. Since sea urchins are of profound value to the extension of human life, gourmet lovers of urchin eggs should seriously consider switching to a diet of white mice instead. Sea urchins are close cousins of sea stars in the Phylum Echinodermata and are referred to as "Echinos", which literally means "hedgehog" or "porcupine" in Greek vocabulary. There are over 800 species of these porcupines, mainly found in tropical and temperate shallow waters and intertidal reefs. Sea urchins have the fundamental body plan of a sea star, including a water vascular system with tube feet, but they also possess a hard chitinous structure with external spines. Mobility is provided by their tube feet, which are longer than those of their relatives. Locomotion is also aided by leverage action provided by spines on the underside, allowing sea urchins to "walk" much faster than sea stars.

Flower from Hell

Anatomically similar to sea stars, urchins also have modified pedicellarae (pincer-like jaw contraptions) among their spines and tube feet. They are the body guards against parasites and other organic larvae which might try to make home on the urchin. These little nipping jaws work tirelessly to remove intruders as well as to pass food particles to the mouth, which is located on the underside. Remember this name ... *Toxopneutes pileolus*. It is a very pretty, short-spined sea urchin with a surface covered by white flower-like pedicillarae with pink tips. Each of these flowers can deliver powerful venom and a smashing pain which results in the paralysis of fish and humans alike. Several human fatalities have been reported from handling these little "flowers from hell".

During daylight, sea urchins live under rocks, coral crevices or in holes securely wedged in position. Any attempt to dislodge them is not only painful, but in most cases futile. As nocturnal feeders they emerge after dark to forage for food before returning to their hideout long before the night is out. For some fishes and other animals, however, a scrumptious feast of urchins is worth the pain. Groupers, triggerfish, crayfish and seals all feed on sea urchins. Most urchins are herbivorous, feeding strictly on algae from rocks and kelp. However, there are some specialised feeders which feed on encrusting organisms, sponges, bryozoans and ascidians. Their feeding mandible is equipped with a well-developed jaw and a set of five enameled teeth, which chew food material before it is digested in a long gut and passed up to an anus opening on the centre of the upper surface. Some species have a spherical semi-translucent cloaca on the anus opening, which probably serves as a garbage bag for waste products.

Elusive sea urchin
Asthenosoma varium
60mm / f22, 1/ 60
Alor, Indonesiai

Cloaca, digestive bag.
Diadema sp.
60mm / f22 , 1/ 60
Banggai, Nth Sulawesi

Purple Heart urchin
Astropyga radiata.
60mm / f22, 1/ 125
Limbe Strait Nth Sulawesi

Diadema setosum takes
over a dynamited reef
14mm / f8 , 1/ 60
Pulau Puan, Sabah

The sea urchin's jaw apparatus is referred to as "Aristotle's Lantern" by natural historians, as it was the Greek philosopher who first described the jaw of the sea urchin as being shaped like the lanterns which were in common use during his time.

THE POWER OF THE SPINES

Sea urchins' spines vary from being short and thick, chalk or pencil-like, to long, thin and needle sharp, or even venom-tipped, as in a few tropical species which have a venomous bulb near the end of the spines. Any divers that have experienced "injections" from sea urchins can attest to the experience being excruciating, similar to that of a hypodermic injection, but with the needles remaining lodged in the flesh for an extended session of agonising, throbbing pain. The Asthenosoma urchins which live in the Indo-Pacific ocean have psychedelic fiery red spines packed with poisonous sacs which rupture upon contact. The punctures guarantee swelling and many sleepless nights.

SAND DOLLARS AND HEART URCHINS

Regular sea urchins, those with rounded skeletal shells, live among rubble, coral rock and sea grass meadows. Two types of "irregular" sea urchins, the sand dollars, which are flatter and oval shaped, and the football-shaped heart urchins, live in sand or mud beds. These characters have short, bristle-like spines.

PROCREATION OF THE PORCUPINES OF THE SEA

As one would imagine, practical sex would be a painful or rather impossible experience for sea urchins. Their young are created by the fusion of sperm and eggs released into the water column. Because the body of a sea urchin is basically a hollow shell, with very little space occupied by organs, a large quantity of eggs and sperm can be manufactured during the breeding season. The gonads of sea urchins may not be lip-smacking delights for fishes, but the Japanese like to indulge in savouring sea urchins' sperm and eggs.

Pencil sea urchin
Theonella cylindrica
60mm / f22, 1/ 125
Kelasey, Nth Sulawesi

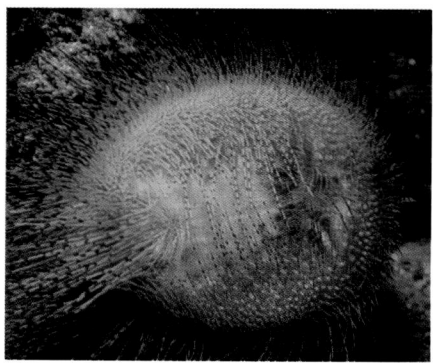

Scrubber sea urchin *Eurypatagus ovalis*
60mm / f16 , 1/ 60 Derawan, Kalimantan

Pincushion sea urchin
Tripneustes gratilla.
60mm / f22, 1/ 60
Moyo Island, Indonesia

Short spined sea urchin
Salmacis belli
60mm / f22 , 1/ 60
Limbe Strait, Nth Sulawesi

SEA CUCUMBERS, CLASS HOLOTHUROIDEA

Humans are far from perfect. We have to close our nose to avoid foul smells and, in doing so, we turn red and might suffocate and die. If you have to live in a smelly environment one day, anus breathing might be the solution. The sea cucumber has perfected this technique. When its anus is not used for the all-important motion of passing faeces, the powerful muscles distend the cloaca to allow water to flow in. Water is pumped into finely branching respiratory trees where gas is exchanged. So when a sea cucumber opens and closes its anus in front of you, it's not being rude, it's only breathing.

Sea cucumbers, or slugs, otherwise known as holothurians, are a kind of echinoderm. Though, physically, they bear little resemblance to sea stars or sea urchins, they do share common traits. They have a water vascular system and most have tube feet. The diversity of form between the 500 known species is ingeniously adapted to their habitats, which range from the coral reef to the deep sea of over 5,000m. Their lifestyles are equally diverse, ranging from, sedentary, slow crawling to active swimming. Their body colours are as variant as their size, with the spectrum extending from sombre neutral through to bright pink, red, yellow and orange.

Holothurians do not have radial symmetry (at least from appearance), but a long body with a head and tail which are sometimes indistinguishable. The majority of holothurians are solidly built, tough and leathery, but some are soft and flaccid, and others, sticky. Skeletal support is provided by microscopic spicules (needles) of calcite embedded in the body wall, as small as one-hundredth of a millimetre in some species.

SEA HOOVER'S VACUUM CLEANERS

Peculiar to their way of life, some species are like vacuum cleaners without dust bags. As they plough through the bottom, large amounts of sand are sucked through their tube-like digestive tract. Edible organic material is absorbed and the processed sand is expelled from the anus, leaving a trail on the bottom.

There are three types of holothurians living on coral reefs. Aspidochirotes are tubular in shape, with leathery skin and tube feet for locomotion. The tube feet around their mouths are specialised tentacles designed to sweep sand particles into the mouth.

Dendrochirotes are similar in shape to the aspidochirotes, but have sticky tentacles for trapping current-borne organisms. Though they are capable of moving, movement is unnecessary because food is home delivered. Apodus holothurians have a body length ranging from a few inches (*Synaptula* 23 cms), found feeding on barrel sponges, to the veritable giant (*Synapta sp*. 6m), found at night foraging openly on reef beds. Apodus have thin, sticky outer skins and move by expanding and contracting their body musculature, aided by tube feet. They have long feeding tentacles.

Sea Apple cucumber
Dendrochinotes sea cucumber
Pseudocolchirus violaceus
60mm / f16 , 1/ 60
Exmouth, Australia

Vacuuming the sea floor - Aspidochirotes sea cucumber
Thelenota ananas, 60mm / f11 , 1/ 60
Ribbon Reef3,GBR, Australia

Dendrochinotes
sea cucumber
Pentacta anceps
60mm / f16 , 1/ 60

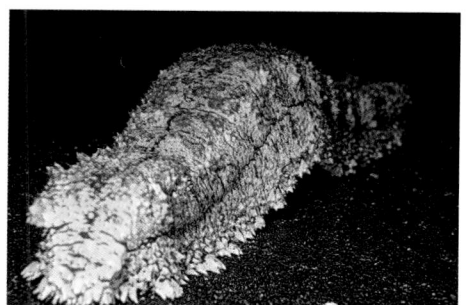

Aspidochirotes sea cucumber
Thelenota anax
60mm / f11 , 1/ 60 Siau, Nth Sulawesi

Apodus 2m long
sea cucumber
Euapta godeffroyi
60mm / f22 , 1/ 60
Mabul, Malaysia

Unique Defence Tactics

Some species of holothurian (*Actinopyga / Bohadschia sp*) possess one of the most unique biological defences in the world. Touch them and you will get into a sticky situation they literally spit their guts at you. These "tubules of cuvier" are regenerated after discharge. The detached tubules are sticky and harden to entangle the intruder in a mesh of adhesive threads. Small crabs and lobster may be rendered helpless and left to die, while bigger animals will be momentarily disabled. Even with such formidable weaponry, however, holothurians are fighting a losing battle with some gluttonous predators - *homo sapien* otherwise also known as the humankind. In Asia, sea cucumber or "trepang" ("beche-de-mer" is the European term) is exhaustively harvested to be made into a tasteless, gelatinous concoction believed to be of aphrodisiac quality by the pea-minded. Incidentally, toxins are found in their body walls and guts.

Sea cucumbers are capable of quick regeneration and restoration of function by a method known as "morphallaxis". By this process the remaining tissues are remodelled to produce a smaller but functional complete animal, which will grow to normal size. The ability of some species to survive and regenerate into a complete animal after being split in half has been documented by the Japanese. In Japanese fisheries literature, there are scattered statements to the effect that, as conservation practice, pieces of trunk of one or more species of *Stichopus* are thrown back into the sea to regenerate when these animals are collected for food.

Sex Think Head!

Yes, holothurian reproduction is done with the head. Holothurians have a single gonad (sex gland in which eggs or sperms develop) which releases eggs or sperm through a gonadpore from the head. In order to increase the success rate, sex is a once a year event and is often synchronised. Males and females convene and raise up, cobra-like, to release sperms and eggs into a chancy fertilisation frenzy. Fertilised embryos metamorphose into free swimming larvae before settling down to assume life as little holothurians. In about 30 species, young are brooded in small pockets in the skin surface, while other species, such as the *Thyone rubra* and *Leptosynnapta* develop the young in their digestive tract (coloem).

Pictures of Cucumbers's Bishop

When you are absolutely bored while diving, sit and stare at the anus of a holothurian , especially those of the *Bohadshia argus*. A scaleless pearlfish (*Carapidae*), a menace from the cucumber's point of view, lives inside the holothurian's gut cavity for protection and to feast on the branchial gills. The fish supposedly enters (tail first) and exits through the holothurian's anus. I have never seen this fish in the wild, but I have many pictures of porcelain crabs entering and exiting sea cucumbers' bottoms. See Tenancy agreement p 144. Holothurians also play host to worms and shrimps.

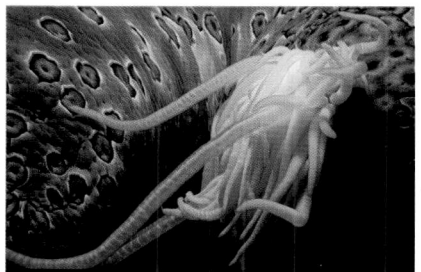

Self defense, spurting its guts
Bohadschia argus
60mm / f16 , 1/ 60
Kelasey, Sulawesi

Spawning -Head raised like a cobra, sperms
and eggs are released
Bohadschia argus
60mm / f16 , 1/ 60 Kelasey, Sulawesi

The nudibranch-like
species
Colochirus robuster
105mm / f16 , 1/ 125
Flores, Indonesia

Predator maybe immobilized to a sticky end!
Bohadschia marmortha
60mm / f16 , 1/ 60
Kelasey, Sulawesi

Worm -like species
found on sponges
Synaptula lamperti
60mm / f11, 1/ 125
Davao, Phillippines

Anal breathing
has its disadvantage
It invites fish and crab to
live up sea cucumber
anuses.
105mm / f22 , 1/ 125

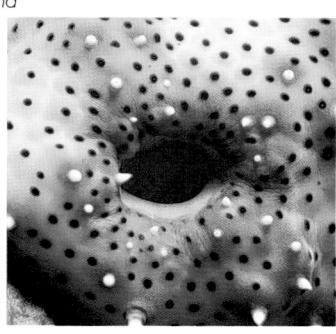

SEA SQUIRTS PHYLUM CHORDATA

One quiet moonless night in 1867, sea squirts took a huge leap in history. Rising from their status as a simple sponge-like animal, they gained recognition as being, in fact, a close relative of modern man. Russian biologist, Alexander Kowalevsky, and his discovery of sea squirts' similarity to mankind, took the scientific world by storm and rewrote the textbooks regarding these simple marine animals. Kowalevsky discovered the existence of a flexible backbone or rudimentary backbone and a dorsal nerve chord in the juvenile form of sea squirts the distinguishing feature of chordates, the *Phylum Chordata* to which MAN belongs.

Sea squirts had at last arrived...and now there are known to be about 1,500 species living in the all world's oceans, found inhabiting coral reefs, caverns, caves, ledges, sand and mud flats and even man-made installations. There are even pelagic sea squirts hanging out in the ocean current with complex natural histories. Sea squirts are also known as "ascidians". This name is derived from the Greek word "askidion" which translates to "leather wine bag", describing the leathery exterior nature of the animal, which takes the form of a tunic, hence the alternative name, "tunicates".

An ascidian body plan is essentially a tough leathery tissue, shaped like a hollow sack. Two tubes or siphons form the openings of the sack and allow water to pass through the pharynx, an internal filtration device lined with microscopic hair-like cilia which create water movement by beating rhythmically to and fro. Some ascidians have a physical appearance similar to sponges, but, when touched, react by compressing their siphons to eject a jet of water, hence the common name "sea squirts" or "cunjevoi" in Australia.

IMPRESSIVE STATISTIC

All simple ascidians have two siphons a mouth or incurrent siphon, and an exhalent siphon. They breathe and eat by drawing a continuous stream of water through the mouth and expelling it out through the smaller siphon. Feeding is performed by trapping plankton through the pharynx, which is equipped with sticky mucus and cilia which beat to generate a current to move food particles to the mouth where they can be eaten. This food filtration device can impressively filter up to 200 litres of water per hour and capture food particles as small as a few thousandths of a millimetre. Waste products are dispersed through the exhalent siphon..

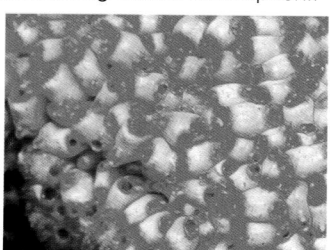

Colonial tunicates
Evsynstyela latericius
60mm / f22, 1/ 60
Maldives

Compound tunicates
Didemid sp.
60mm / f22, 1/ 125
Pulisang, Nth Sulawesi

Solitary tunicate
Rhopalaea sp.
105mm / f22, 1/ 125
Bontang, East Kalimantan

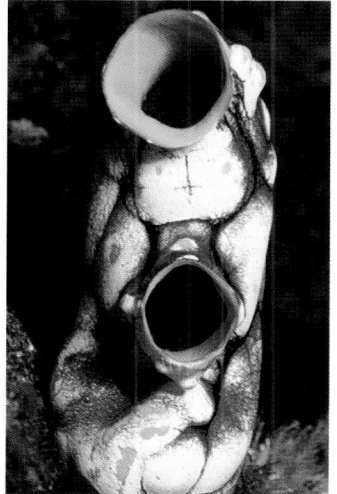

Solitary tunicate
Not the inhalent and exhalent siphon.
Polycarpa aurata.
60mm / f22, 1/ 60
Flores, Indonesia

Colonial tunicates
Evsynstysla latericius
60mm / f22, 1/ 60
Maldives

Posies Under the Sea

Colonies of ascidians, hydroids and sponges frequently live closely together to form some of the most beautiful posy arrangements of the sea. Ascidians exist as solitary animals or as colonies. Solitary species contain one individual living in one tunic whereas, in colonies or social species, many animals share one tunic a commune of ascidians. Individuals living in colonies are called zooids and are connected by branches which allow blood to flow between them. Compound species are an interesting lot. Having realised that it is probably more productive to share common "anuses", or exhalent siphons, they are easily distinguished by their few large aperture siphons among many smaller siphons. There is, however, much more interdependence between zooids living in compound colonies.

While solitary individuals come no bigger than 20cm, colonies come in every conceivable shape, regular and irregular, and a variety of sizes. They may be shaped like an upright tulip-like bunch, or bunched together like grapes, cones, spheres, or in flat sheets and plates. In some species, the zooids are completely embedded in matrix form or partially embedded in a lamellae material. Colonies expand as the zooids within them clone themselves by budding and dividing.

Unless they are located in high current, the body surface of solitary ascidians becomes real estate for sponges, hydroids and sometimes even barnacles. Compound ascidians, on the other hand, with their numerous inhalents, would probably suck in any juvenile larvae which settle on them.

Sex and Sensibilities

Being sessile animals, sex couldn't be an exciting exercise for ascidians. Solitary species procreate sexually by timing the release of eggs and sperm through their exhalent siphons, hoping for random fertilisation to occur. Most species are hermaphrodites. They possess both male and female gonads and can produce both eggs and sperm. As self-fertilisation is a bad idea, it is avoided by the successive maturation of male and female organs. Some colonial species are internally fertilised, though how the sperm enters the parenting zooids without being caught as food remains an enigma to the scientific world. The embryoes are incubated internally to become free swimming larvae, before being released into the water, increasing the probability of survival. Most species produce vast quantities of larvae to compensate for high mortality rates. The free swimming larvae quickly metamorphose into tadpoles (tailed larvae) and remain non-feeding until they find a suitable site to settle on. As suitable plots are rare and scarce, many perish. The lucky few that find ground to attach themselves to literally stand on their face, glued to the surface with an adhesive structure called papillae. Since, as a sedentary adult, a tail would be a total waste of time, the larvae's tails are quickly sheared off, while feeding structures, siphons, and pharynxes develop, enabling the young ascidians to either colonise or live out a solitary life. Colonial species can also procreate by cloning themselves through a process of asexual budding.

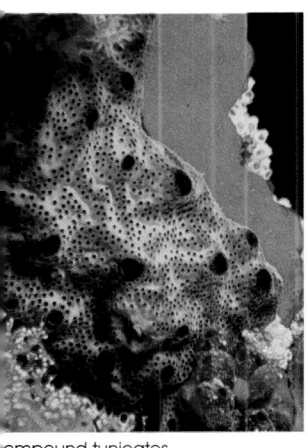

ompound tunicates
demnum sp.
)mm / f22 , 1/ 60
mbe Strait, Nth Sulawesi

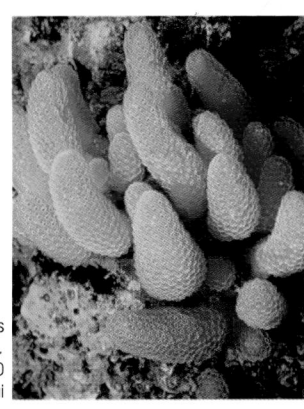

Club tunicates
Sycozoa sp.
60mm / f16 , 1/ 60
Loloda, Indonesiai

Compound tunicates
Diplosoma virens
60mm / f16 , 1/ 60
GBR, Australia

Solitary tunicates
Clavelina robusta (black)
&
Rhopalaea sp.
60mm / f22 , 1/ 60
Bunaken, Nth Sulawesi

ASCIDIANS EMPLOYED AS POLLUTION OFFICERS

Being filtration feeders, scientists have found some species of ascidian to be efficient indicators of pollutants in the ocean environment. While *Microcosmus sulcata* has demonstrated the ability to concentrate heavy metals, cobalt, zinc, chromium and selenium, the cosmopolitan species *Ciona intestinalis* is an effective indicator of iron build-up in water. Other species have been found to trace accumulation of scandium, antimony and other harmful pollution elements. Thus, ascidians, though looking nothing like humans, are employed by environmental biologists to police the refuse of mankind.

SEA POSY PICTURES

Taking pictures of ascidians can be addictive for a marine photographer. There are never enough of them and the next posy always looks better than the last. Twin powerful strobes are recommended. Use f22 / f32 to enable maximum depth of field in posy images. Search for neutral backgrounds to bring out details and textures in the bouquet. They make great "wow" pictures.

Compund tunicates
Atrolum robustum
*this specie often
confused as
Didemnum molle
60mm / f22, 1/ 125
Layang Layang, Malaysia

Sea posies
Atrolum robustum
& *Clavelina moluccensis*
60mm / f22, 1/ 125
Alor, Indonesia

Slender stalk tunicates (rare)
Perophora namei
60mm / f22, 1/125
Tukang Besi, Indonesia

Colony on sea fan
Perophora modificata
60mm / f16, 1/60
PNG

Ecteinascidia loandaensis
60mm / f22, 1/60
Pulisang, Nth Sulawesi

Single colonies
Clavelina robusta
60mm / f16, 1/60
Manado Tua, Nth Sulawesi

Sea posies
mostly
Didemnum sp.
60mm / f22, 1/60
Kakaban, East Kalimantan

TENANCY AGREEMENTS IN THE SEA

Have you ever wondered why suckerfish (remoras) attach themselves to the under-bellies of sharks and rays? Are they just hitch-hikers or has a pact or unwritten tenancy agreement been made between the two species? Which of the two parties stands to benefit the most from this living arrangement? Is there some form of "fish currency" changing fins, or does this exchange of services work on a barter system? Perhaps the shark advertised in the local paper "Suckers wanted for cleaning chores and regular body massage... Husband and wife team preferred, remuneration by way of free anchorage, occasional scraps and exciting travel opportunities ...call G White".

The different living arrangements which animals have evolved over millions of years, form part of nature's rich web of self-generation. Within this web, a category of animals exist that live together in a unique relationship referred to as "symbiosis", a term initiated by the French naturalist de Barry. His description is used to describe animals of different species which live in affiliation with one another. Symbiotic relationships occur when two dissimilar animals live together, whether it be for protection, food sharing, home sharing, mobility or just plain old companionship. Usually, one of the partners is larger than the other and plays a more or less passive role, such as the shark. This partner is referred to as the "host". The smaller, more active partner (the suckerfish), is known as the "symbiont". While the host may be found without its symbiont, the symbiont is rarely found without its host. In some symbiotic relationships, host and symbiont are totally inseparable.

The most well known of living arrangements in the marine world is between clownfish and anemones. While the clownfish are known to tend to the removal of parasites and to the general cleaning of their host, the anemone, in turn, provides a safe haven for these clownfish families; where they eat, sleep and breed. This form of relationship, where hosts and symbionts benefit from one another, is described as "mutualism". Marine scientists also use the term "commensalism" to describe animals which co-exist simply for the purpose of eating together. The word commensalism is derived from a Latin word literally meaning "sharing the table" or "dining together". Sea cucumbers and their multiple companions of worms, crabs and the pearlfish (which live up its anus) are prime examples of commensalism. In these relationships, it would appear that the plodding sea cucumber gains nothing while its travelling companions gain a home and food. I am sure sea cucumbers are not amused when scientists start probing or squeezing their behinds for the pearlfishes and crabs!

In reality, the reasons behind such living arrangements cannot be attributed to any one particular factor. Currently, the conditions under which such tenancy agreements arise are not fully understood, but one can only marvel at an evolutionary process which has been able to produce such complex, finely balanced yet highly successful associations. The interaction and inter-dependency of life upon this planet forms part of a very sophisticated yet fragile web of existence; this means that the extinction of any one species affects the ecosystem in its entirety. Human understanding of the many tenancy agreements in the marine world is a quantum leap forward in the efforts of preservation.

The most bizarre feature of clownfish is their immunity to the anemone's stinging cells (nematocysts), whose slightest touch would paralyse other fishes. They are not born with an instant immunity, but they acquire it by picking up a substance from the mucus-coated tentacles that prevents the nematocyst from firing. A newly born fish, or one that has become separated from its host anemone for too long, must acclimatise itself to the stinging cells by rubbing its body up against the tentacles, in order to coat itself with the anemone's mucus. Once the acclimatisation has been completed, the clownfish becomes fully immune to the sting and can spend unlimited time in the arms of its host. This is nature's way of ensuring a constant and continuing bond between fish and anemone. Completely reliant on their landlord for protection, clownfish will disappear quickly into their safe haven upon any hint of danger. Within the relationship, the anemone is clearly seen as the "big brother" of the two, by providing the fish with a secure home. Although it has not been proven, the anemone is said to benefit from the housecleaning duties provided by its tenant. While an anemone can survive happily on its own, a clownfish is never seen without an anemone.

PINK SKUNK CLOWNFISH (AMPHIPRION PERIDERAION) WITH PURPLE MAGNIFICENT ANEMONE (HETERACTIS MAGNIFICA).
60MM / F16 1/60, NAIN, NTH SULAWESI

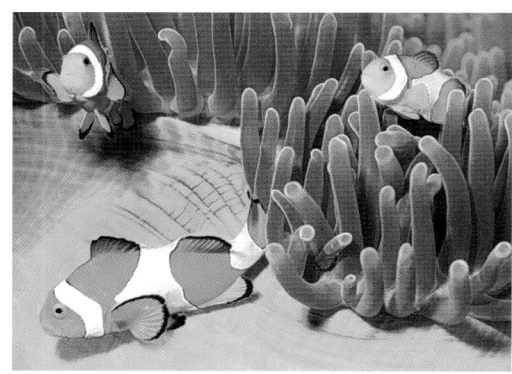

ORANGE CLOWNFISH (AMPHIPRION OCELLARIS) WITH PURPLE MAGNIFICENT ANEMONE (HETERACTIS MAGNIFICA).
60MM / F16 1/60, BUNAKEN, NTH SULAWESI

Feeding on zooplankton that floats past, anemones provide the clownfish with an additional food source. Clownfish dine on the leftover morsels as well as algae which may grow upon the anemone's tentacles and oral disc, which, if left, might otherwise cause disease. The base of an anemone is a safe haven for a nest and spawning, while additional protection for clownfishes' eggs is provided by the anemone's waving, embracing tentacles.

Emperor Shrimps living with nudibranchs have been described as an "Ageism" (Morton); that is, an association for protection, or even transport, through camouflage. Brightly coloured nudibranchs escape predation in a most ingenious way. Their bodies are toxic, or extremely distasteful, due to their diet which varies from anemones and algae, to hydroids. Larger animals are simply warned off from sampling these soft bodied animals by their foul odour. Spanish Dancer nudibranchs are perfect hosts for Red Emperor Shrimps, offering them both protection and transportation to feed on sea bed detritus. The similarity in colour of both host and symbiont makes the shrimp almost invisible. The shrimp may also acquire additional nourishment from the mucus covering of its host. Nature has a most amazing way of ensuring the survival of her animals through camouflage. When a pair of Emperor Shrimps are found on the maroonish purple pleurobranch, they are of exactly the same colour. If we were to ponder at what point in time their tenancy agreement began, most of us would probably fail to reach a conclusion, and more than likely, would come up with more questions than answers.

EMPEROR SHRIMP
(PERICLIMENES IMPERATOR)
AND SPANISH DANCER
(HEXABRANCHUS
SANGUINEUS)
60MM / F16 1/60,
KELASEY, NTH SULAWESI

EMPEROR SHRIMP
(PERICLIMENES IMPERATOR)
AND PLEUROBRANCH
(PLEUROBRANCHUS GRANDIS)
60MM / F22 1/60,
PULISANG, NTH SULAWESI

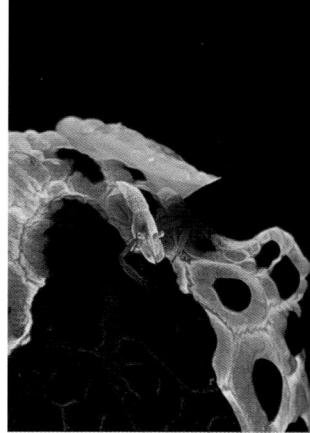

One of the most fascinating symbiotic relationships in the marine world is between the ill-sighted Alpheidae shrimp and its "watch dog" goby. Among sand patches of the Indo-Pacific reefs, it is common to find pistol shrimps and gobies (*Amblyeleotris*, *Cryptocentrus sp.*) sharing burrows. While the shrimp works through the day excavating and maintaining the burrow by keeping it free of loose rubble and sand, the goby stands guard at its entrance. At the first sign of danger the fish will dive into the burrow and cause the fortress to collapse. Once the goby feels that it is safe enough, it will return to the entrance of the burrow. If the coast is clear, a flick of its tail signals to the shrimp that it is safe enough to re-emerge. The shrimp will then begin restructuring and cleaning the burrow all over again. While the shrimp does all of the housework, the goby brings home morsels from the reef and, if too large to swallow whole, the shrimp is often imposed upon to perform the duties of a domestic food processor. Even though shrimps are able to scavenge through the goby's leftovers, it seems that the goby has the better deal within this relationship.

BLACK CHESTED GOBY (AMBLYELEOTRIS GUTTATA)
AND PISTOL SHRIMP (ALPHEUS SP.)
105MM / F11 1/60, DERWAN, EAST KALIMANTAN

There can be no safer refuge in the ocean for a tiny crustacean than up the anus of a sea cucumber. An association in which one animal lives within another, doing the host no harm but using it as a permanent address, is described as "inquilinism". Both the commensal crab (*Lissocarcinus species*) and pearlfish (*Carapidae family*) are often found protruding from the anus of sea cucumbers. The protection given by the host is obvious, but the symbionts also benefit from the life style of a sea cucumber. Crawling along the sea bed, sea cucumbers consume a huge amount of sediment in a single day. By living amidst its food tracts, the symbiont receives a constant supply of organically rich nutrients and a stream of oxygenated water. With free meals, air-conditioning, travel, and a safe home, there is nothing to be embarrassed about by living up someone's behind.

In most Indo-Pacific reefs, sea cucumbers are indiscriminately harvested for the beche-de-mer industry. Homes for pearlfishes and the tiny swimmers crabs are thus becoming short in supply. Their survival within the marine environment is under serious threat.

Harlequin Crab (*Lissocarcinus orbicularis*) and Sea Cucumber (*Bohadschia marmorata*)
60mm / f22 1/60,
Kelasey, Nth Sulawesi

PORCELAIN CRAB
(LISSOCARCINUS SP.) AND
NOBLE SEA CUCUMBER
(HOLOTHURIA NOBILIS)
60MM / F16 1/60,
MAKALAHE, NTH SULAWESI

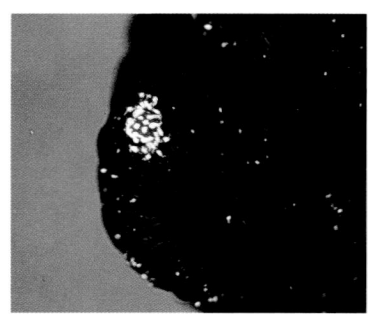

The Claws Among a Sticky Anemone (Anemone Crab and Sticky Anemone)

One could easily mistake the frantic scissor-like action of the claws of the Porcelain Anemone Crab for that of a stylist trimming and shaping the tentacles of its host anemone. Nothing could be further from the truth. In reality, the two claws and their modified appendages (maxillidpeds) are in fact their feeding utensils which are alternately flung in and out, in a rhythmical manner, in order to catch plankton and suspended sediments. Porcelain Anemone Crabs (usually a male and female) are frequently found living in an endoetic arrangement with several species of sea anemones. Like the relationship between clownfish and anemone, the crab is completely immune to the stinging tentacles of the anemone which can paralyse or even kill a larger crustacean. These intrepid little crabs often scuttle amidst and under the anemone, and even enter into its mouth and stomach with impunity. While the anemone offers these porcelain crabs a protected home, playground and protection, it is doubtful if there are any benefits at all to the host.

Porcelain Anemone Crab (*Neopetrolisthes ohshimai*) and Mertens' Sticky Anemone (*Stichodactyla mertensii*).
105mm / f11 1/60,
Bunaken, Nth Sulawesi

An Easy-going Relationship (Ambion Shrimp and Anemone)

The commensal Ambion Shrimps are perhaps the least specific in their selection of a host. The Ambion Shrimp has a distinctive body pattern and they display their behind by holding their abdomen and tail in a vertical position and rhythmically flicking it up and down. This animal is characteristically easy-going and can be found in seven different species of anemones. They have also been observed taking shelter among mushroom corals (*Heliofungia sp.*) and plate corals (*Montipora sp.*). When harassed, or when imminent danger is detected, the shrimps will immediately scramble beneath their host. A generous anemone may sometimes provide refuge for a family of up to ten Ambion shrimps amongst its tentacles and underside.

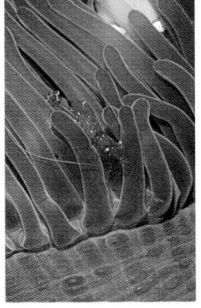

Anemone shrimp (*Periclimenes holthuisi*) and and Mannifica Anemone (*Heteractis magnifica*)
105mm / f11 1/60,
Bunaken, Nth Sulawesi

The Ambion Shrimp (*Thor amboinensis*) and host anemone (*H. Magnifica*).
105mm / f11 1/60,
Mabul, Malaysia

Living on Stars

(Clingfishes, Squat Lobsters Living with Feather Stars)

Feather stars have the ability to literally "fly" around the reef, settling with their bird-like claws (cirri) on coral outcrops, or gorgonian fans that are directly in the current flow. Waving their feathery arms which are equipped with sticky fine tentacles (pinnules), they are able to trap planktonic organisms drifting past. The tit-bits are then transferred down a special food gutter in each arm to the central axis, where the mouth is located.

Some marine animals are lucky to live among feather stars. Symbionts are not only offered protection and regular embraces but, by hanging around the centre disc area, they are ensured of a continuous food supply, without unduly upsetting their host. Feather stars play hosts to crabs, shrimps, clingfishes, squat lobsters and even worms.

Another remarkable trick performed by symbionts in this relationship is known as "colour morphism"; the act of assuming the colour of the host. In response to the host's pigmentation, clingfishes living on Yellow Noble Crinoids are characterised by a series of light and dark yellow bands. We can safely assume that the juvenile Elegant Squat Lobster on picture M1 will quickly metamorphose into the same colour of its host. Elegant squat lobsters living with yellow feather stars have previously been observed to be of exactly the same colour as their host.

The interaction and inter-dependency of life upon this planet forms part of a very sophisticated yet fragile web of existence. This means that the extinction of any one species affects the ecosystem in its entirety. Understanding the many tenancy agreements in the marine world is a quantum leap forward in efforts of preservation.

Clingfish *(Discostrema crinophila)* and Yellow Noble Crinoid *(Comanthina nobilis)*
60mm / f22 1/60,
Manado Tua,
Nth Sulawesi

Spider crab *(Naxioides taurus)* and
Feather Star *(Oxycomanthus sp.)*
60mm / f22 1/60,
Alor, Indonesia

Crinoid shrimp *(periclimenes
tenuis)* and
Yellow Noble Crinoid
(Comanthina nobilis)
* note the colour that shrimp has
assumed
105mm / f22 1/60,
Alor, Indonesia

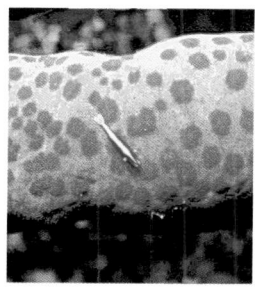

Sea star shrimp (*Perilclimenes
soror*) and host Linckia star (*Linckia
laevigata*)
105mm / f11 1/60,
Batuna Reef, Malaysia

Squat lobster *(Allogalathea elegans)* and
Feather Star *(Oxycomanthus sp.)*
105mm / f11 1/60, Taka bona rate, Indonesia

Potential prey of *Epitonium billeeanum* is the sunflower coloured *Tubastraea coccinea* widely distributed throughout the tropics. Since Tubastraea are not dependent on sunlight, they are mostly found in overhangs, caves and along steep walls. Their tentacles are equipped with stinging cells used in trapping plankton in passing currents.

In the scheme of bedtime stories and fairy tales, wolves are victims to the necessity of life they need to eat to live. The wolf in sheep's clothing is just being ingenuous but by doing so is condemned for it's natural instinct and craftiness. It is, after all, nothing personal against old grandma or the cute little damsel but everything to do with hunger and staying alive. But of course, the big bad wolves got the bad end of the deal; albeit a bad reputation and having to put up with a song of mockery, they are gradually becoming extinct in the real world. Extinction caused by the kin of little Red Riding Hood

In the marine kingdom, there is a particular trickster with plenty of attitude as well intelligence. A nimble spirit not wishing to be considered amongst the ordinary folk they have, so to speak, emulated the 'bad wolf in the sheep's clothing antic'. These 'bad wolves' of the sea don cheerful canary yellow suit, complete with a seemingly innocent appearance, but they are notorious for literally sucking the daylight out of their living prey, and thereafter using their victims cadaver as nest for their offspring. Ingeniously their fertilized eggs are a perfect mimicry of the deceased tissue and tentacles. Terrors of Tinseltown would have been impressed.

In my undersea sojourns through the Indo-Pacific waters I have had several encounters with these Molluskan of the sea but luckily they are only tiny, ridiculously minute otherwise I would not have lived to write you this eyewitness story of their clandestine behavoir.

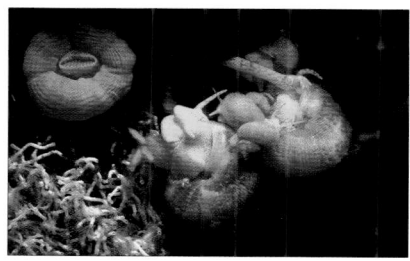

Our little bad wolf is the *Epitonium billeeanum*, specie of marine snail belonging to the family of wentletraps. Discerning in their culinary pursuit, they feed exclusively on Tubastraea, a hard brightly orange and yellow coloured tube coral found in the reefs of Indo-Pacific Ocean. In the society of Billeeanum the male is smaller, and is capable of performing the two essential chores in evolution to eat and procreate at the same time.

Few of us are capable of eating while procreating but the female *Epitonium billeeanum* has no problem performing this feat. Even when depositing eggs on a deceased they continue to feed on another victim. Note the yellow egg-mass is deposited in strings of tiny yellow whirls and loops that resemble extended Tubastraea at close range. By mimicking the stinging tentacles of the anemone, the brood is well protected from other predators. Epitonium billeeanum are known to have a hefty appetite. After an invasion by a flock of Epitonium billeeanum, few polyps escape the massacre. An entire colony maybe wiped out in an afternoon.

Once their prey is located, *Epitonium billeeanum* proceed to devour their prey by sucking out their tissue. Male and females generally feast on separate Tubastraea polyps but may occasionally dine on a single victim, sort of wining and dining before going to bed. In an effort to evade and protect themselves from the enemies, the tubastraea polyps are retracted. In is unclear to the scientific world whether the snails are immune to the stinging cell of their prey, however with a powerful rubbery proboscis the *Epitonium billeeanum* is able to keep a safe distance from any stinging tentacles. The snail in this picture has commenced its meal on the still-living coral, while its neighbours have met their fate.

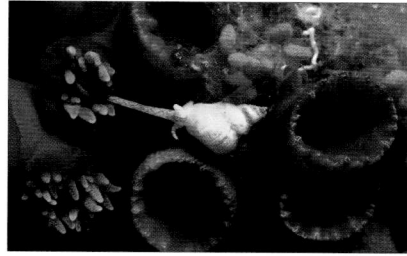

Epitonium billeeanum are generally found singularly on the reef and by nature's biological clock they convene to mate and feast.

Threats to Coral Reefs

CORAL BLEACHING

This is a phenomenon where the corals on a reef turn white, then many of them die, most frequently due to unusually high water temperatures, but also from various other effects, including unusually low temperature. The most severe and extensive coral bleaching ever recorded was in the Indian and western Pacific Ocean during 1998, and was observed to be associated with the very strong *El Nino* effect operating that year.

Corals are living animals; hence they require energy (organic nutrients) and building materials (calcium and oxygen) for growth. These requirements for survival are met by corals in a **symbiotic** relationship whereby sunlight and inorganic carbon is converted into useable products by tiny plants called zooxanthellae that live within the corals. If this relationship between animal and plant is disrupted, for example by marked changes in water temperature, nutrient levels, suspended sediments, fresh water or light levels in the water over the reef, the stressed animal will expel the plants. Without the zooxanthellae, the corals turn white (or white tinged with a little pink or blue colouring from their tissues), in a process known as bleaching. If the change persists, the coral tissue dies.

In some circumstances only the exposed parts of the coral colony die, leaving some parts to lead recovery when conditions return to normal. In other cases, whole corals die, leaving huge dead patches on a reef.

DIVER DAMAGE

As a diver and educated user of the reef it is important to be aware of your role as a passive observer of nature. SCUBA diving and snorkelling are not contact sports! Corals should never be touched, stood upon, or used to aid diver stabilization. This is particularly important for the many fragile species of *Acropora*, which break only too easily.

A responsible reef user understands the cumulative impact of tourism pressure and respects our passive role on the reef by using the following simple strategies:

Adjust your buoyancy so that you float over the corals rather than land on them! Watch your fins so you don't break corals with them.

Try to use dive boats that store human waste so that it can be treated properly back on shore rather than dumped into reef waters.

Anchors cause small impacts that can add up over time. Anchors should be lowered over sandy areas - which are usually obvious from surface by the colour of water. This also ensures they don't get stuck!

CORAL DISEASES

Corals are subject to various viral and bacterial diseases, which can spread just as they do in human populations. The most common of these are "black band" and "white band" disease, both of which can affect Staghorn Corals. They act by killing the tissue of the coral in a band which spreads from the branch tip downwards. In black band disease, the dying part of the branch has a dark black colouration. The reason why corals are subject to these diseases is unknown, but it is thought that they are associated with pollution or a reef that is in a generally "unhealthy" state because of some other impact. The diseases were first noticed in the Caribbean during the 1970s, but they have now been seen in the Indian and Pacific Oceans.

CROWN OF THORNS SEA STAR

The crown of thorns sea star, *Acanthaster planci*, eats hard coral tissues, leaving only the dead skeleton in place. Feeding by crown of thorns is a natural phenomenon, and when the sea stars are only in small numbers they play an important ecological role in terms of opening up new space on the reef, and promoting diversity. However, crown of thorns is considered to be a serious threat to the survival of coral reefs when large feeding aggregations occur and kill a high proportion of all the corals on a reef. After more than thirty years of investigation, there is still no consensus as to what causes the crown of thorns numbers to increase relatively suddenly. The consequences of large scale crown of thorns predation range from possible extinction of species to a loss of tourism trade, decrease in fishery outputs, decrease in available coral seed stocks, reef erosion and algal takeover.

POLLUTION

Patterns and processes between land and sea environments are interconnected. What starts out (or is thrown out!) on land often ends up in the ocean and since corals usually inhabit the waters close to the coast they are often among the first to be affected by human activities on land. Agriculture, industry, cities and development all produce great, obvious changes to the landscape but they often come with a hidden impact on the seascapes of the waters nearby.

Nutrients from fertiliser run-off, sewage and industrial discharge are one of the major impacts, harming the corals which are adapted to low-nutrient conditions while promoting unchecked growth of algae which smother the reefs. Increased sediment run-off, from agriculture and development also add to the corals' burden, interfering with their ability to feed, breathe and obtain light. These impacts are often quite insidious so that reefs can quietly slip away over a period of decades, gradually thinning and losing their diversity of corals and other reef animals so that only those divers with long memories notice a difference.

DESTRUCTIVE FISHING

Many coral reefs bear the brunt of heavy human pressures. Fish bombing is perhaps the worst of these activities - explosives are thrown from boats and the explosions stun and kill much of the life below. Because fish have swim bladders they alone float to the surface when dead and are collected by the waiting fishermen. While corals are not the target of this fishing, the explosions have a devastating effect on them, reducing them to dead rubble. Local people miss out in this desperate business, as the destroyed reef ceases to produce fish for future meals.

By actively supporting the preservation of natural patterns and processes on land and in the sea, divers can help to ensure the natural checks and balances account for changes in the coral reef habitat.

Dr Carden Wallace

Tropical Reef Fishes

A handy 'getting to know' learning and identification guide for reef fishes in 3 colour coded segments - easy, simple and straightforward. Get acquainted with reef fishes, where they live, how they live, what they eat plus all the lucid secrets of sex in the sea. Tropical Reef Fishes takes you beyond the academia, translating scientific jargon into laymans language. Over 500 sharp colourful pictures, supported by concise informative descriptions indicating distribution, size, common and scientific names, habitat and exposure details. 160 pages With Tips for fish photography - Top Seller - Complete New Edition - US$15

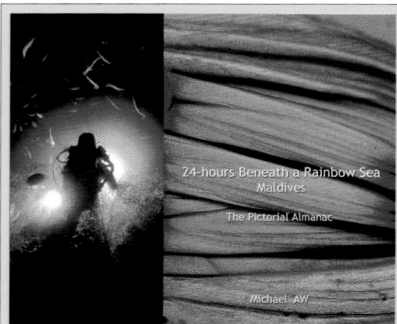

Limited edition / autographed copy
US$55

"24 Hours Beneath a Rainbow Sea" is unique, the almanac is a documentary of a day in the life of a submerged reef system as seen through the eyes of the 24-hour dive team. All the images are actually captured between 10 to 11 April 1999. The energy and enchantment of a marine reserve in the Maldives is beautifully revealed in a celebration of artistic imagery. Learn the intricacies and idiosyncrasies of sharks, octopus, eels, snappers, turtles, clownfish and their neighbourhood of critters. Relive the 24-hour odyssey in a metropolis of marine animals and indulge in the glory and colours of Planet Earth's rainbow realm. A " Gift of State" high quality limited edition

OneOcean Portraits Book

16 high quality ready to frame 10" x12" prints of reef fishes and dolphins. Award Winning Images.

Free Gift screen saver WIN 95/98/2000/ ME of all the images. A$25 / US$20

To order any of the above fax or e-mail with name, address, phone/fax number, e-mail. Payment by bank cheque or VISA / Master cards. Include expiry date and billing address. Postage not included.

OceanNEnvironment
Fax: 61 2 9686 3688
E-mail:oneocean@OceanNEnvironment.com.au
Www.OceanNEnvironment.com.au

OceanNEnvironment is a non-profit organization listed with the Registrar of Environmental Australia. The mission of OceanNEnvironment promotes and initiates preservation projects as well as endeavors to document the status of coral reefs, biodiversity and the impact of man-made pollution through research programs and educational expeditions. OceanNEnvironment provides lectures and educational material to schools, private clubs and other non-profit organizations. Associates of OceanNEnvironment are volunteers comprising of award-winning underwater filmmakers, photographers, marine biologists, researchers and writers dedicated to produce high quality natural history multi-media works. Our objective is to present information about our natural heritage in an exciting and thought provoking manner. Our aim is to motivate people to learn, to love and to help preserve our natural world.

Key issues on our immediate agenda are lobbying for restriction of export of Cheilinus undulatus Maori Wrasse to the live-fish trade in Hong Kong, Napwatch Program in the Maldives, sea turtles hatcheries in Sri Lanka and Indonesia and the Save Our Sharks campaign in Singapore. The OceanNEnvironment SOS fund, established in 1998, is committed to the conservation and preservation of the aquatic environment and its resources. Our long term goal is to educate the younger generation about the importance and responsibility of preserving the marine environment by developing and disseminating educational materials, marine awareness seminars, campaigns, sea life festival and promoting industry effort at a "grass root" level that yield measurable result. The organization provides direct financial support or campaign for funding to support worth while endeavour, performance base projects and networking relationship with other organizations to strengthen common goals.

Please Contribute to our Save Our Seas Fund

Premium Membership US$35 pa
Benefits:

Friend of OceanNEnvironment Wall Certificate
Membership Card
One 8"x10" limited edition canvas print or
Free Screen Saver Rainbow Sea Edition CD
Discount on OceanNEnvironment expeditions
10% discount of on merchandise from:
Asian Geographic Explorer Club and
www.OceanNEnvironment.com.au
Invitation to special expeditions and seminars
Pay US$68 and the package includes one year subscription to Asian Geographic magazine Apply with Name, postal address, phone and fax number, e-mail address.
Send payment by check or VISA/Mastercard details to
OceanNEnvironment
PO BOX 2138, Carlingford Court, Carlingford NSW 2118 Australia
Fax: 61 2 9686 3688 email: info@OceanNEnvironment.com.au
www.OceanNEnvironment.com.au

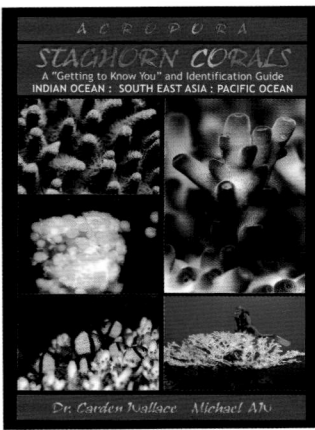

This book is the most comprehensive of its kind that is not produced specially for coral biologists but a guide for those in other scientific disciplines and yet easy to use for the budding naturalist. Staghorn Corals are the foundation of tropical coral reefs; they are the most widespread and common of reef-building corals. They occur in a multitude of shapes, from simple, stumpy fingers through to elegant tables, feathery spirals and giant plates. This book is a pictorial testimony to that incredible range with photographs and descriptions of species along with information on where they are found and how to identify them. "Staghorn Corals" also gives you an insight into the life of these animals with sections describing how they grow and organise their colonies, their bizarre life-cycles and their microscopic features. Written in a non-jargon style, "Staghorn Corals" is a must for divers, snorkellers underwater photographers, students or simply those with an interest in the coral reefs of the world. US$15

Staghorn Corals
Indian Ocean:
South East Asia : Pacific Ocean
Dr. Carden Wallace / Michael AW

Dive Log
of My Underwater Adventures

This new Scuba logbook really stands out from the rest; more than just a logbook it features a colour portfolio of some of the most vivid images from the sea. Images are categorized in fishes, invertebrates and marine mammals. Additionally the contents include First Aid for Serious Diving Emergencies & Accident Management, How to avoid Decompression Sickness, Diving Hazards & Diving with Computers, information on conservation issues as well as 100 log pages with generous space for documenting all your observations. 175mm x 130mm sized, perfect bound and laminated for the discerning diver.

US$9 plus $1 postage anywhere in the world; Order with VISA or Mastercards. Please include number, expiry date and billing address. Trade price applicable to dive shops and instructors
Contact: oneocean@OceanNEnvironment.com.au or
Fax: 61 (0)2 9686 3688

How to Be A Responsible Diver

When on diving holidays, choose to patronize only resorts and live-aboard vessels with operational standards that go beyond just being environmentally conscious, but ones that actively contribute to the sustain ability and preservation of the marine environment.

Do not patronize restaurants that serve shark fin soup, Napoleon wrasse (Cheilinus undulatus) and live reef fish imported from countries known to have problems with fish collected using sodium cyanide. Educate yourself about the source of the seafood you choose to eat.

Purchase diving equipment from manufacturers that contribute to the welfare of the ocean.

Write and complain to magazines, newspapers or book publishers who publish pictures that show animal harassment or articles that are ecologically offensive. Remember, it is because of you that they exist - tell them when they are wrong.

Learn more about marine animals by attending marine ecology programs and participate in eco-tourism or research diving expeditions. But most importantly participate in programs that take an active interaction with local people - in form of education, training and directly or indirectly benefiting their livelihood.

Do not throw anything into the sea, even if it is bio-degradable. Even if it is legal, set an exemplary example by not removing anything such as shells, corals or fish either dead or alive from the sea.

Report to relevant authorities any observation of damage or practices that could be damaging to the marine environment.

Support marine protected areas such as Marine Parks.

Share your experience, have passion, don't be afraid to stand up for your cause.

Invest in education; awareness of the intricacies of our planet is as critical as life itself; only when we understand, then we can appreciate and have the passion to preserve.

Spanish Dancer's gills

About the Author

Michael AW is a photo-journalist based in Sydney, he specialises in wildlife, environmental and travel features. His articles and photographs have been featured in publications spanning from Australia, Asia and Europe to the USA, including, Asian Geographic, TIMES, NATURE Focus, GEO, Ocean Realm, Scuba Diver and Action Asia to name but a few. Over 20,000 of his photographs have been published and he has won many national and international awards including the BBC Wildlife and three times the Nikon International Photographic competition. Michael is also the initiator of the METAMORPHOSEA project, the first in the world to dive and record the activity of life on one coral head over a 24 hour period using oxygen enriched air in 1995. He has presented lectures at DEMA, Monterey Bay Aquarium and the Singapore National Library as well as to The Australian Museum Society.

Michael & his wife Alison Redhead are the principals of OceanNEnvironment, a non-profit public company dedicated to preserve the quality of the marine environment. Their work is committed to enhancing awareness of the beauty and fragility of the natural environment. Check Out www.michaelaw.com